The author, writing under the pseudonym Robert Clifford, is a retired general practitioner. His medical practice has been successfully combined with writing and broadcasting. A Yorkshireman by birth, he now lives in Oxfordshire and has three grown-up children and four grandchildren.

An Arrow Full of Quivers

A Collection of Short Stories,
Anecdotes, Deep Thoughts,
Fables and Bits of Fun

DR ROBERT CLIFFORD

WARNER BOOKS

A *Warner* Book

First published in Great Britain in 1995
by Little, Brown and Company
This edition published in 1996 by Warner Books

A CIP catalogue record for this book
is available from the British Library.

ISBN 0 7515 1180 3

Typeset by Solidus (Bristol) Limited
Printed and bound in Great Britain by Clays Ltd, St. Ives plc

Warner Books
A Division of
Little, Brown and Company (UK)
Brettenham House
Lancaster Place
London WC2E 7EN

This book is dedicated to the memory of the late
MURIEL DRAKE, a teacher at Bideford
(North Devon) School for thirty-eight years.
She has helped so many,
and is constantly in our thoughts.

Contents

Contents

Deep Thoughts

Courage

Travel and Adventure

Fables

Short Stories

Finale

Acknowledgements

My grateful thanks to Warner Books (Little, Brown UK) for permission to publish extracts from:

JUST HERE, DOCTOR
NOT THERE, DOCTOR
ON HOLIDAY AGAIN, DOCTOR?
YOU'RE STILL A DOCTOR, DOCTOR!

Previous Publications of Contents

Stained Reputations	Radio Oxford
How to Survive Women	*Mother* Magazine
How to Choose Your Mate (Men)	*Escort* Magazine
	Pelham, Sphere, Warner and Ulyerscroft Editions of *You're Still a Doctor, Doctor!*
Nothing to Wear (1960)	*Mother* Magazine

Acknowledgements

A Desirable Residence	*Rostrum* Magazine *Mother* Magazine
The Art of Nearly Going To	BBC 'You and Yours' programme *Rostrum* Magazine Pelham, Sphere, Warner and Ulverscroft Editions of *On Holiday Again, Doctor?*
When There's a Doctor in the House	*Mother* Magazine
First-Aid Examination	*Rostrum* Magazine
Psst! Read Any Good Books Lately? (1974)	*Medical News*
Where Do Elephants Go to Die?	*Escort* Magazine
The Three Wise Men	'Woman's Hour' BBC Radio Oxford *Douai* Magazine *Flints* Magazine
Soliloquy at Evening Surgery	*Pulse* Magazine
Ben Fellowes	'Home For Today' BBC *Argosy* Magazine BBC Radio Oxford White Lion, Pelham, Sphere, Warner, Ulverscroft and Chivers Audio Editions of *Just Here, Doctor*
The Available Gentleman	BBC Radio Bristol 'Home This Afternoon'

Acknowledgements

	Argosy Magazine BBC Radio Oxford Pelham, Sphere, Warner and Ulverscroft Editions of *Not There, Doctor*
Television Set	'Woman's Hour' BBC *Argosy* Magazine BBC Radio Oxford White Lion, Pelham, Sphere, Warner, Ulverscroft and Chivers Audio Editions of *Just Here, Doctor*
Vive le Rugby!	*St Mary's Hospital Gazette* *Medical News*
The Eight Men from Niger	*Flints* Magazine
Thirty Years Gone	*Confrontation* – the magazine of Long Island University USA
The Queen's Champion	*Escort* Magazine
The Bridge	*Flints* Magazine
Communications	BBC Radio Oxford *Flints* Magazine
The Man in the White Cotton Gloves	BBC Radio Oxford *Flints* Magazine
Playing at Writing	*P.E.N. Broadsheet* *Medical News* *St Mary's Hospital Gazette* *Facets* – the magazine of the Sinodun Writers BBC Radio Oxford

Introduction

To find a title for this miscellaneous collection of short stories, articles, fables and experiences was extremely difficult.

After much pondering I, like Archimedes in his bath, suddenly arose with the shout 'Eureka!' on my lips.

The *Yorkshire Ridings Magazine*, who hold a number of literary lunches and dinners each year, have always been very kind to me – not that I'm any great shakes as an author, but have, after a lifetime's experience in medicine, collected a number of amusing medical anecdotes, many of them vulgar, which when linked together as an after-lunch or after-dinner speech will on most occasions be funny enough to ripple the attending diners' gravy.

Although a minor author, it did give me an entree to mix with my peers on literary dining occasions as a sort of aperitif to the big guns who followed me.

One day Joan Laprelle, Features Editor of the *Yorkshire Ridings Magazine*, rang to ask if I would like to share lunch and dinner with the great David Bellamy.

The dates were going to be difficult and I felt I would be really out of my class with him, so I hesitated. 'Or,' she said, 'we have a lunch and a dinner in Barnsley during the Barnsley Book Week.' This was a new venture intended to somehow blitzkrieg the town with books.

Foolishly, without enquiring who the other authors might be, I readily accepted. It was only when I arrived at Barnsley some months later that I realised what I'd let myself in for.

I found my fellow speakers at the dinner were to be James Herriot and Jeffrey Archer, and at lunch the following day, John Braine and again Jeffrey Archer.

The following report by 'Mandrake' of the *Sunday Telegraph* gives a better account of the dinner than I can.

'Dr Clifford, the first speaker, prefaced his remarks by saying that he was glad to be back. It transpired that in 1945, straight from Epsom College, he'd gone down the local pit as a Bevin Boy. At a Foyle's lunch there would have been five minutes' applause; in Barnsley no one moved a muscle – why clap someone for doing what they'd been doing all day?

'Jeffrey Archer spoke rather in the manner of a head boy giving a vote of thanks to the governors on a speech day, largely upon the number of books he'd sold in America, but he got the applause due to being a former MP.

'Mr Herriot had them eating out of his hand. He told how, when in New York, he had read a highly intellectual review of his latest book which said, "Mr Herriot has the gift of spinning charm out of the ordinary."

'Back in Yorkshire a week or so later an old farmer friend had said, "Y'know, your books are all about nowt." "I like to hear the same thing said different ways," he said, sitting down to rapturous applause.'

The lunch next day was different. John Braine, an old friend, replaced James Herriot in the batting order. I had invited some guests, too – my cousin Edna and her husband Rowley, who lived quite close to Barnsley.

Edna's late father, my Uncle George, who used to live in another South Yorkshire town called Maltby, had been very good to me when I was a Bevin Boy at Dinnington colliery at the end of the war. I was determined to say something nice about Uncle George during my after-lunch speech, and Uncle George and Maltby were rattling round in my head as I enjoyed the excellent food. As usual, I opened the batting for the speakers and launched off in fine style.

'Ladies and gentlemen, this is my first visit to Maltby . . .' I was about half way through my third side-splitting medical anecdote when one half of my mind said to the other, you do realise that you said Maltby instead of Barnsley – and somehow I made a clumsy and inglorious retreat from this catastrophic opening, got through the rest of my speech as best and as quickly as I could, then tried to hide behind a dinner menu when John Braine stood up and took over.

It was a day when John was brilliant and I was soon forgotten. I'd heard John speak many times; he was never a poor speaker and being in Yorkshire, on home territory, he seemed to find another dimension. There was almost a standing ovation.

This just left Jeffrey Archer as the last man in. I had heard it said that Jeffrey Archer always gave the same prepared speech and if you'd heard him once, there was no need to hear him again. On this day he proved how wrong this was. He gave a brilliant, completely off-the-cuff speech without a single note – it was totally spontaneous. The full fifteen minutes was taken up on the theme that he had understood from his publisher, his secretary, his back-up team, the *Yorkshire Ridings Magazine*, the hall porter etc., that he had come to speak in Barnsley. Now having arrived, he learns from the first speaker that he's actually in a place called Maltby, which in fact he's never heard of before. It is difficult to try and hide fourteen stone of person behind a lunch menu, but I did my best.

Eventually, after what seemed like two hours, he stopped speaking. We all then went off and did our own book signing on separate tables, getting together afterwards to present each other with a copy of our own book, as is traditional at these affairs.

I think John Braine gave me *Stay With Me Till the Morning*, and Jeffrey Archer, who is quite a nice chap really, gave me his latest book, of which he said he was most proud, a collection of short stories called *A Quiver Full of Arrows*.

Writing in my study, my eye caught the jacket of this book and it was then I realised that if I'd been in the bath like Archimedes, I would have jumped out of it shouting as he did. If *A Quiver Full of Arrows* is good enough for a book of Jeffrey Archer's short stories, why not *An Arrow Full of Quivers* for mine?

So with many thanks to Lord Archer for the inspiration, I hereby name this book *An Arrow Full of Quivers* – God bless her and all who sail in her.

Bits of Fun

1. Stained Reputations

9 was to be lunched in London by a senior lady at the BBC, prior to a live broadcast on a *Woman's Hour* programme on medical matters.

It was always an adventure to travel up from the West Country to do a broadcast.

It was a hot summer and to mark the occasion I had invested in a light-weight cream linen suit. I was much slimmer in those days and really fancied myself in my new outfit.

I was glad I had bothered to dress up as my BBC host took me to a very smart restaurant.

After some smoked salmon, I chose the chicken Kiev as my main course.

Knowing she was lunching a country yokel, my BBC friend warned me about my chosen dish.

'Do be careful,' she said, 'otherwise you might get a spurt of hot garlic butter over your nice suit.'

Of course I didn't need to be told this – I had dined out before. So before cutting into the giant portion of chicken I made a few tentative blow holes with my fork.

My BBC lady looked on approvingly – perhaps I wasn't so rustic after all.

However, the first cautious incision with my knife was a disaster: a boiling-hot stream of garlic butter shot into my lap (to identify the landing area more accurately, I had the distinct feeling that my nether regions were being cooked in boiling oil, which they probably were).

The whole of the front of my cream linen trousers was covered in steaming garlic butter.

I looked as if I had been incontinent for about two weeks – with the additional aroma of garlic as a sort of smoke screen.

Various waiters and my embarrassed host made efforts to sponge me down with a variety of fluids. These, however, did not touch the garlic butter, but just extended the stained area.

There was no way I could go home quickly and change – I had a broadcast and a long train journey back to the West Country still ahead of me. Leaving the restaurant, the BBC lady walked in front of me, whilst to hide my affliction I casually dangled a half-open newspaper in front of me.

Somehow I got through my broadcast, helped by being able to hide my middle behind the table on which the microphone stood (although I did notice at one stage that the technicians turned on some special extractor fans).

The journey home was a nightmare. I travelled through London with my dispatch case firmly clasped in front of me, and sat on the train chain-smoking cigars and with a newspaper on my lap.

I thought I had fooled everybody, but in a very short time I had the compartment to myself.

Even in the taxi home from the station, the driver

said, 'Just back from France, Guv?'

This event had a profound effect on me for years afterwards – I never went anywhere without a spare pair of trousers in my briefcase. Most times this passed unnoticed, but occasionally when delving for a hidden paper at meetings, I had to pull out the trousers to retrieve the elusive document. Eyebrows would shoot up.

At medical meetings it was assumed that I was a candidate for an early prostatectomy. At lay meetings all sorts of interpretations were put upon this habit.

When I retired and moved to the Thames Valley I thought I would soon be in great demand as an after-dinner speaker. However, it wasn't until I had been there a few years and had written a book about the local town that I had my first invitation.

I was to speak to a group of civic dignitaries and their wives at a Christmas dinner at a posh hotel overlooking the river, a few miles out of the town.

It was a splendid occasion, and I was seated in a place of honour next to the distinguished chairman in his full regalia and chains of office.

We had just been served our soup when the chairman got up to make an announcement. As he rose to speak he accidentally caught a full bottle of red wine with his elbow, tipping over the entire contents right in front of me – in fact, over my soup and my jacket, and of course the major portion went into my lap. I had a feeling of *déja vu*. Repairing to the toilet I found that I now had pink cuffs on my white shirt, that I was very damp in my nether regions (but not as damaged as I was with the garlic butter), and that I smelled like a wino (which of course I expect I was). Fortunately I was wearing a dark suit, and hoped that when I got up to speak the table would hide most of the damage.

However, when the dinner finished I found I was to speak from a platform in an adjoining lecture room. All my damp patches would be in view.

Fortunately, the civic dignitaries were both dignified and civil, and although the vast majority had no idea why I reeked of claret, nobody made any comment.

I obviously hadn't blotted my copybook, as in quick succession after this talk I was asked to speak at a Rotary Club lunch, a Round Table dinner, a dinner run by the wives of the 41 Club, the Evergreens and a meeting of massed Women's Institutes. But, I had learnt my lesson: determined to have no further stains on my reputation I now keep a spare pair of trousers in my car.

2. How to Survive Women

Somewhere in the Ural Mountains in Russia is a man aged 160 who is still going strong, and a mere lad of 105 in the same community has just married again for the fourth time. It would appear that this group has succeeded where all the males in the rest of the western hemisphere have failed: that is, they have learned how to survive and understand women.

Talking to one of the most happily married men I have ever met, on his golden wedding day, I asked him what his thoughts were. He said he no more understood his wife now than on the first day he married her.

Women, without a doubt, are the unfathomable sex, and it is amazing how we males survive.

The female logic is quite baffling. When I was coal-mining, the whole female community lived all week with their hair in rows of brightly coloured plastic rollers encased in nets, and only removed them for three glorious hours at the Saturday night dance when, if seen as a group from behind, they could have been mistaken for a flock of permanently waved sheep.

By early Sunday morning all the defences had been rebuilt and I was never sure whether to congratulate them on their hair or the uniformity of their rollers.

In numbers I feel overwhelmed: national statistics say there are ten women to every nine men. But if I'm ever called to a confinement, or go to a christening or a family do at Christmas, the ratio is always apparently ten to one. There seem to be about ten aunts to every uncle, and 1899 must have been a vintage year for grandmothers though the grandfathers' crops must have had the wrong fertiliser.

It is very difficult to get a standard pattern of behaviour or response from the opposite sex. An agonised scream from my small daughter usually means her doll's house has fallen over, but if she calls quietly, 'Daddy, will you come down when you have finished shaving?' it probably means that my eldest son has broken his leg!

My wife will worry all week that she has lost three-pence somewhere in the supermarket, then spends £3 on a hat that she never wears because she doesn't like it.

My secretary is easier to understand because I have got used to her. When she brings my mid-morning cup of tea and news of how the surgery is going, a frown and 'Everything is terrible' means that she has laddered her tights and there are only two patients to see; whereas a smile and 'Everything is fine' means that the hair salon has managed to fit her in after all and there are forty-two patients in various stages of decay in the waiting-room.

Evenings out, when my wife has to dress up, are one of the worst hazards. All day I will be getting steady reminders like, 'Don't be late,' or 'Don't have any confinements because we have to be out at eight.' So I rush through my work, dare any of my pregnant women to go into labour, arrive home at 7.30, bath, shave, change, and am ready and waiting at 7.55 only to find my wife is not dressed, hasn't done her face and doesn't want to be the first to arrive anyway.

On holidays I fare a bit better because, having two sons, we men stick together and give the appearance of numbers.

On a boating trip we broke even with three males against mother, daughter and grandma. But when camping we were one down with three against mother, daughter, and aunties Margaret and Sally. But nobody seems to take any notice of me, and if we three males sneak off to go fishing or play cricket we aren't even missed.

One year, hoping to get away from it all, I went to a writers' summer school. I arrived in the middle of the opening speech to hear the lady chairman say how pleased she was that the number of men attending had increased to a record figure. The statistics didn't look good, though – of the 380 attending, 68 were male, 310 were female and 2 would need further scrutiny to determine which sex they belonged to.

I thought, till last night, that I had no chance of surviving this unequal struggle. My wife came in and said, 'Who was the tall blonde we saw in the film last night?'

'Elizabeth Taylor,' I said.

'Yes,' said my wife, 'that's her.'

'But Elizabeth Taylor isn't tall and she's dark,' I said.

'Oh, but you knew who I meant,' said my wife.

Unconsciously I think I'm winning.

3. How to Choose Your Mate (Men)

Anatomically the best wives are stocky, wide-hipped, thick-waisted, full-chested members of the female sex, with short strong fingers, powerful backs, tremendous stamina and of the belief that £1 shouldn't be wasted on the housekeeping when it could just as easily be spent on beer and fags (cigarettes).

With this in mind the average male will look for the slimmest, fragile, most expensive looking bird (woman) he can find. The main factors influencing his decision being the size, mobility and shape of the soft tissue swellings on the front of the female thorax (chest), and the length, curvature, muscle balance of the trunk body-supports (the legs). The main vote going in a ratio of three to two to the legs or undercarriage.

Pursue the bird (woman) object of your desire for forty-eight hours. Then stop. If you go beyond this time period she will lose all interest as she will think she has got you, and will put you down in her book as another conquest and then devote her time to trying to pick up her best-friend's boy, who is an inch shorter than her and has never so much as looked at her.

After the initial forty-eight hours start paying attention to the object bird's (woman's) best friend, who has a pleasant face but whose undercarriage doesn't fill your desired specification.

This changes your bird (woman) from being on the point of giving you up to deciding that you are all she ever wanted. She will fling herself at your feet, thus changing her from the austere, wonderful, unapproachable beauty that you were first attracted to, to something available and humiliatingly easy that you immediately lose interest in.

As the friend that you have been chatting up (in spite of her bad legs) shows no reciprocal interest, because she has just become engaged, you find her the most irresistible female you have ever seen. And if she marries this chap who has swinishly tricked her into wearing his ring, life will hold nothing for you and you will apply for a job as a porter in Albert Schweitzer's leper colony.

If she is fool enough to break off her engagement for you, forty-eight hours after the initial victory, she will fall into the same category as the first bird (woman) and you will realise how mad you were to have considered having anything to do with a bird (woman) with legs like hers.

Your first bird (woman) will then have got over her disappointment with you and paired herself off with some other swine, and immediately will recapture all her old allure.

You will then fling yourself at her, but now that you are so available, you become less attractive. Thus she won't have anything to do with you, unless of course you start chatting up her second-best friend, then the whole cycle will repeat itself.

These permutations are great fun for a few years, but if by the age of seventy-five you have not broken the cycle, even though the citations of individual cases will prove me wrong, it is unlikely that this article will be of much use to you.

If you were able to remember back to the alluring stage, when a bird (woman) is humiliating herself at your feet, then it would be possible actually to pick for your own whichever bird (woman) you really wanted, but of course it never works out like this.

The best thing is to marry the girl next door, if she will have you, as there is no doubt it's the birds (women) who decide on who is going to be their mate – the average man has no say in the matter at all.

4. Nothing to Wear (1960)

My wife must surely claim to be one of the most poorly dressed women on record. I am able to assess this from the number of times she says, 'I have nothing to wear.'

What I cannot understand is that over the years we have been married, my share of the wardrobe has steadily decreased until now half of my clothes are downstairs in one of my son's rooms.

This is inconvenient, as I have two suits that look very similar and after one cross-match hanging I surprised Mrs B., our daily, when I rushed down in my top half looking for the missing bottom.

The main problem with clothes, of course, is money.

Every couple of years I go off exploring deserts, and my wife in her turn has a shopping week when she goes up to London with a friend to see how quickly she is able to get through money. She gets more proficient each year and so far I have never been able to give her enough to last her the course. But I do my best, remembering it's not difficult to make her chilly about the Sahara.

I think the durability of clothes bought nowadays must be poor, and have come to this conclusion after attending two weddings within four weeks of one another. As I expected, my wife had nothing to wear for the first wedding and got herself all kitted out anew. She liked these particular clothes so much that she wore them twenty-four hours a day for three weeks, but just before the second wedding, only four weeks later, she was back in the state of having nothing to wear.

It was just after this that, prompted by my bank manager, we had a family discussion on clothing finances.

My wife had a brilliant idea. She would go to sewing classes and make most of her own and our daughter's (aged five) clothes. And think what a saving that would be!

She came back all fired up after her first lesson, with a book of patterns and a sewing-machine catalogue. I viewed the catalogue with grave suspicion.

I said, 'The book of patterns I understand, but you already have a sewing-machine.'

'Oh,' she said nonchalantly, 'my teacher says to do proper work I must have a swing-needle machine otherwise I can't do button-holes, embroidery or zig-zag stitch.'

I could feel my bank balance begin to zig-zag.

She followed this up by '. . . and I'm afraid I'll just have to buy a steam-iron as well, but once I get organised clothing bills should fade away.'

Looking quickly at my now blood-less face she added, 'I hope first to make you a new safari sleeping-bag. I would hate you to be cold at night, and think how nice it would be to have something I'd made with you.'

I will admit she worked hard, making at least two

dresses a year for herself and three or four for Jane, our daughter, and there was some consolation that the sewing-machine is guaranteed for twenty-five years.

I did once half-heartedly think of suggesting that as she could now make her own clothes she wouldn't need her London trip; but I thought better of it.

The price of these expeditions still goes up, in spite of home production, and when I query this, both my wife and her friend Marcia, who accompanies her, turn on me in unison and say, 'But everybody knows everything's going up.'

As I write these lines, propped on my office desk is a wedding invitation. I will ring home and prove my point.

I: 'Darling, we have been asked to the Taylor's wedding on the fifteenth, can we make it?'

Wife: 'Yes, darling, I think so, but I'm afraid I've nothing to wear.'

5. A Desirable Residence

Having three children and the experience of several house moves, we were able, before choosing our present home, to know exactly what accommodation we really required.

Not for us the mistake of having the television in the main sitting-room, with nowhere for the children to play, or the radio in the same room as the television, with wars of attrition going on within the family.

We were fortunate enough to purchase a roomy Jacobean house with a surfeit of reception rooms. It had been a doctor's surgery, and its waiting-room made an ideal games room, housing the battered half-sized billiard table that I had inherited from my grandfather.

There was a dining room and two lounges, and each of the children had a large bedroom. This made life easy.

We put the television in the second lounge, making it a family room. (Unfortunately, the TV did have to share with the piano.) The first lounge had the radio, and we had the games room as an outlet. Smugly we could reflect on the people who hadn't been as thoughtful or as well organised as we were.

At the time of our move my second son became interested in war games. This required that our revered billiard table be covered in a plywood sheet so that he could manoeuvre the Roundheads against the Cavaliers, or the Spanish against the French, or whatever. But no matter which battle he was fighting, no one was allowed to touch the set-up, so the games room was immediately lost for general use.

The great disadvantage of having the television and radio in separate rooms had not yet become obvious. If you turned on the radio in lounge one, which adjoins lounge two, you had to turn up the sound on the TV set in lounge two so as not to be drowned by the radio; whereupon, of course, the radio listeners in lounge one turned up the volume of the radio so as not to be drowned by the television.

Whilst this was going on my young daughter would invariably decide that she hadn't done her music practice and, despite the radio and television hullabaloo, would begin her piano lessons.

My oldest son, a keen and capable trumpeter who has always had the incredible faculty of being able to do two things at once, found he could sit on the stairs and practise his trumpet while watching the television in lounge two if somebody left the doors open. As I am a busy medical practitioner, the phone would be ringing about every ten to fifteen minutes.

Son number two, the war-gamer, tiring of his rather juvenile activities but not wanting them to be disturbed, decided to become a musician like his brother and took up the guitar. Being even more able than his brother, he found that he could play his guitar with either the radio blaring or the television flashing.

On several occasions I have found myself in a madhouse with the radio and television competing at full blast, my daughter playing the piano in the corner, son number one playing the trumpet on the stairs, son number two playing the guitar on the settee, the dog barking, the telephone ringing, and somebody at the front door collecting medicines – and the sounds peaked whenever the adjacent doors from the two lounges were opened for either the radio listeners to catch a glimpse of the TV, or the TV-ers to catch a few chords from the radio.

I have now put an advertisement in the local newspaper for a house with one reception room, no electricity or gas, no telephone or front doorbell, and one that specifically forbids children. I am prepared to swop this with a delightful old Jacobean house with an excess of reception rooms and a preponderance of power points.

6. The Art of Nearly Going To

One of the available counter-inflationary methods as yet not used is the much neglected art of nearly going somewhere. Over the years, this art has lapsed into a decline, and a planned resurgence could be enough to restore economic stability to this country.

Nearly going somewhere is not as simple as it might seem. At present I am planning nearly to go to Moscow next October with the friend who inspired this article. It is not enough to carry this thought in one's mind; one has to make the usual planned approach as if one were organising some bona fide visitation.

When planning to nearly go somewhere certain steps are essential.

Carelessness can cause havoc.

For example, there is no point preparing nearly to go somewhere with an out-of-date passport, as the situation could arise where you might actually have to go somewhere and need your passport. This not only prevents you from being able to appreciate nearly going to places in future but, particularly if this was to be a business trip, it could mark the end of your employment.

The ideal passport is a surrendered one with the corner clipped off, which everybody knows is no use at all.

In applying for travel brochures when making your plans, it is no use going to the travel agency; instead search the back of your desk for last year's brochures where different dates and prices are quoted, but make sure that they include all the anticipatory blurb to whet your appetite about the place you nearly go to.

In planning your date, the time to arrange a 'Nearly went to' is when you have some prior commitment. For example, if you want nearly to go to Paris, try and fix the dates to coincide with your admission to hospital for the removal of your gall bladder.

The main benefits of nearly going somewhere are of course the saving of money and the preserving of friendships. Not having to pay is a good way of not spending, and it is on holiday that you most often quarrel with your friends. Nowadays, of course, there is the additional benefit that if you never leave your back garden the chances of being held hostage by an Arab hijacker are very small. An added bonus is achieved if you can persuade someone to pair up with you in the pursuance of this art. If, for example, you are able to say 'Jimmy Savile and I nearly went to Majorca last year' not only will you be an instant success at any party, but all your colleagues will stand in awe of you.

Nearly going somewhere has been a tradition in my family, and it has been a matter of family honour, when planning these trips, to go industriously about it with all the already described paraphernalia. This has enriched our family heritage as now I have an aunt who says she was nearly on the Titanic; my grandfather, who says he was nearly in the San Francisco earthquake and, more recently, my eldest nephew who was nearly in Rome when the late Pope died.

Most of our family folklore is based on situations that members of the family were nearly present at, and it has only been by diligent book-keeping that they have been able to show how near they were to being there.

For anyone who decides that he is nearly going to go somewhere, one hundred per cent physical fitness is essential. Regular exercise, clean living habits, abstinence from smoking and consumption of alcohol, and regular medical check-ups are a must. For unless you are actually fit enough nearly to go somewhere there is really no point in nearly going anywhere at all.

I am looking forward to my proposed trip in October, which will be ideal preparation for nearly attending the next Olympic Games.

Mainly Medical

7. Touch-line Doctor

As Medical Officer to Drakes College, it was not part of my duties to have to attend rugby matches, but as a rugby fanatic, having spent all my medical student days playing rugby (learning my medicine after I had qualified), I indulged my obsession by being a self-appointed, very vocal touch judge to the college's 1st XV.

It had been a poor season. Drakes College was a smaller than usual public school and hence had a more limited choice of players than most, and for some reason (probably the school food) it never had any big forwards. All matches started with the disadvantage of playing against taller, heavier opponents so, although the college lost most of their matches, pound for pound they were probably as good as any side in the country.

The match they *had* to win was the annual fixture with White Cliff College, who came touring pre-Easter from Ireland. This was a school of the same size, and its pupils matched Drakes' in height, weight and religion.

Today's match was a particularly tough one. It was

thirteen-all with five minutes to go and, in spite of all my vocal encouragement, to date the Drakes College left wing and potential match winner had not received a single clear pass throughout the whole game.

Fed up, in the dying moments of the game, he took the initiative, dived into a loose scrum, picked out the ball, headed back to his position on the wing and started to make his lonely journey towards the opponents' try line.

Inspired, I almost kept pace with him, racing along the touch line, forgetting the thirty years between us. There were about ten yards to go to the line when, out of the blue, appeared a rocket-propelled opponent, his radar inextricably locked on to the Drakes College wing. There was to be no escape; obviously this opponent had a rapier missile somewhere in his family tree.

Now fully involved in the action, a second before impact I dropped my touch-line flag and screamed 'Pass!' to the helpless wing. As a reflex to my scream, and in the process of being scythed down, he sent me a perfect pass, which I caught in full flight. I charged on instinctively and scored in the corner. My pleasure in this achievement was cut short by a huge snorting referee, who bellowed, 'Keep in touch, Doctor'. He disallowed my try and awarded a penalty, which led to a line-out – which led to a try. Having been so near to victory, Drakes College were now left to chalk up one more defeat. Without my intervention it would probably have been at least a draw.

There were mutterings from the team, the headmaster and a bevy of those who had almost been proud parents – 'Why doesn't he stick to medicine, however bad he is at it?' being the most popular phrase.

My only supporters were the White Cliff team, who

asked me to sign the rugby ball as a souvenir. Subsequently a senior boy was elected touch judge and I was relegated to being just a vocal spectator, not even team doctor.

The medical problems of the 1st XV were the concern of the school matron, who was supposed to be present on the touch line at all 1st XV matches. She rarely referred a case to me; anything beyond her ken was immediately whipped off to hospital by ambulance. My duties were strictly confined to the sick-bay and sanatorium.

It is a characteristic of boarding-school matrons that they are birds of passage. It is rare for one to stay more than two or three years at any one school. As one of them said to me, if you are not already mad when you take the job, you certainly are by the time you finish it.

Of the matrons who came and went during my twenty-year stay at Drakes College, one of the most memorable was Matron Smith. She was a tall (six foot) fifteen-stone matriarch of the old school, who must have terrified probationers, and never let house-surgeons have a cup of coffee on her wards in her hospital days. Her ward would have been spotless. She was the type whose departure we longed for, but when it eventually came left a hiatus that was never filled, and a level of nursing standards that was never reached again. Matron Smith did not like either the cold or rugby matches, and on cold days would risk being called to an emergency, closeting herself in her sitting-room before a huge coal fire.

One very cold day, a serious emergency arose, almost certainly a broken leg. I, as Medical Officer to the school and the best qualified spectator, offered my services, but these were immediately turned down by both sides with a 'No, we must wait for Matron.' (They were probably remembering my days as a touch judge.)

Matron was summoned, and we turned in awe to watch her running the four-hundred yards from her quarters, medical case clasped to her ample bosom, splints in one hand, bandages and a bottle in the other, her cape billowing behind her in full flight. If Kitchener had employed her at Khartoum, he wouldn't have had to fire a shot. The games master, who was standing next to me, said sotto voce to no one, 'God! I would like to see someone tackle her.' Almost before the words had left his mouth, a small boy detached himself from the crowd and sped towards the approaching matron. He executed one of the best cover tackles I have ever seen. You could feel the earth shake as she hit the deck – bottles, bandages and splints flying in all directions.

We all rushed towards her, even the boy who had the suspected broken leg. We crowded round in a circle as she slowly caught her breath. There didn't seem to be too much damage – that was the best of it – but what fireworks were going to emerge? This would almost certainly lead to her resignation.

She sat up as she recovered her equilibrium, adjusted the skirt of her dress, and to her eternal credit took the whole thing in good part. She looked me straight in the eye, saying, 'I guess you and I could start a team together, Doctor.'

She didn't resign, stayed on at least another year then returned to her beloved hospital work, where I expect she terrorised everyone – but without a doubt would have had the best ward of any hospital that was fortunate enough to employ her.

Matron was one of the many types of 'touch-line doctors' I was to come across in a long medical career.

For some reason team sports very rarely encourage doctors to attend to their medical wants during games. They much prefer the Red Cross, St John's, physiotherapists or nurses, but the most popular of all is the sponge-and-bucket man – he is the tops as far as games players are concerned.

This can be confirmed by watching robust team games on television, whatever the level of play, even up to internationals. A player being knocked unconscious for over five minutes will eventually force the referee to reluctantly summon the sponge-and-bucket man, using a type of semaphore that only referees and presumably sponge-and-bucket men understand. Now if the referee had called a doctor (and, of course, he would have to be a specially trained doctor, as no medical colleague I know has even the rudiments of semaphore), the doctor would have placed the player in what is known as the recovery position, made sure his airway was patent (i.e. he could breathe), called for a stretcher, then summoned an ambulance. He would probably keep the player in hospital for a week and ban him from playing again for at least three weeks. The sponge-and-bucket men are made of sterner stuff: a good slap round the face with a wet sponge will have most men back in the game. However, if this fails the player is pulled to his feet, the sponge-and-bucket man then drops the tools of his trade and grabs the ears of the offending player and either twists or pulls them (whether it is a twist or a pull, I don't know – it's a trade secret). You can bet that in two minutes the patient will be fit and conscious and returning to his position on the field. (I was never taught ear-pulling as a medical student; my guess is that it is some subtle form of Western acupuncture.)

I was once knocked unconscious when playing rugby

as a medical student, actually against Rugby Football Club on the morning of a Twickenham rugby international. Being surrounded by doctors and embryo doctors, I was of course sent to hospital for a week and not allowed either to read or watch TV (I made a rug), and was banned from playing for a further three weeks. My girlfriend and my mother, who were watching, were terribly impressed by the concerned crowd of medics who rushed towards them as I was whisked away in an ambulance. They were much less impressed when they found the reason for all the 'concern' – had they now got tickets for the afternoon's international which they wouldn't be using?

In addition to medical help from the touch line, many games teams have a nominated medic as an actual member of the team. If there is any medical catastrophe on the pitch, he is immediately called in as a consultant. He is usually bald, above the average age of the rest of the team and 'has seen most things before'. His specific qualification in most cases is his ability to drink a pint of beer in under three seconds. Only occasionally have these men had conventional medical or first-aid training. They are the only people whom I have seen overrule the bucket-and-sponge brigade, and most have acquired the skill of ear-pulling/twisting of the aforementioned.

One of the cruellest acts I was party to as a teenager occurred when playing for the under-thirteen cricket team. Our wicket keeper, Jack Brownson, because of age and inexperience was not protected by such aids as a box and shin pads. Obscured from the direction of one of my fast balls by the batsman, he received this hard piece of leather 'smack' at full speed in the middle of his etceteras. It brought tears to our eyes as well as his. We helped

30

him gingerly off the field and laid him gently in the shade of a tree. Although we were a very junior team, we had our own team medic, one Lance Sparrow. Lance was in fact aged sixteen and was backward in everything except smoking, drinking and women. Academically, he was at the same level or just below the average thirteen-year-old, so he was relegated to the under-thirteen cricket team.

We stood back in a semi-circle round the prostrate Jack. Lance strode forward to make his diagnosis. With one glance he both summed up the situation and prescribed a treatment.

'Sloanes liniment,' he said authoritatively, 'well rubbed in,' then he walked round to the other side of the tree to have a cigarette.

Jack limped off back to the school. It was only at supper time we realised he was missing. Search parties were sent out, and at last he was found, sitting on his bed in the dormitory, eyes screwed up in agony. His right hand was clutching a glass of cold water, into which he had somehow managed to insert his etceteras.

Matron was called, and there was calamine lotion, bathing and pain-killers for him. We were all lectured about our cruel deed, most of us bewildered. We were all given a drop of liniment to try – and certainly it left me with a lasting memory. We did not have to sack Lance Sparrow as team medic – as it turned out, the next day he was discovered to have made one of the dining-room maids a teeny bit pregnant, and so was expelled on the spot.

8. When There's a Doctor in the House

The doctor is a hero in many households, and some patients even say that it is sufficient for him to walk into the sick room to put them halfway on the road to complete recovery.

One place that a doctor's magic does not seem to hold good, however, is in his own home, where the opinion of the domestic help, the gardener or the man next door is much more important than that of the qualified expert.

My own wife consults all the do-it-yourself home health guides, and will tell me exactly what I ought to do for the children. When my mother is staying the old dear expects full details of how I should treat various conditions, then tells me how she thinks her own doctor would have treated them differently. She once even offered to show me how to fill in an international certificate for smallpox vaccination as she was sure I was doing it quite the wrong way.

Doctors either over-treat or under-treat their own families. There seems to be nothing in between. You will find one doctor's family being attended by a stream of consultant colleagues and having all the rarest complicated obstetric histories, and specialists come to deal with any malady that should befall any of them. The more trivial the complaint, the deeper the possible significance.

The doctor who under-treats his family will blissfully play cricket with his fourteen-year-old son, not realising that the poor lad whose bowling is off today is actually showing the classic signs of lobar pneumonia.

In the casualty department of one hospital I met a middle-aged doctor almost in tears. He had just brought his daughter in, having been unsuccessful in stopping her diarrhoea over a period of four days. She had asked, 'Could I go and see a proper doctor, Daddy?'

Some doctors' children are practically weaned on the different types of antibiotics, and if there were such a thing as a penicillin sandwich it would certainly be part of their regular diet. Others, however, reach the age of twenty-one thinking that aspirin is the only available treatment for any disease.

The real trouble is that to his own family a doctor is just an ordinary person, whereas real doctors they believe are superior, detached human beings, who know all the answers. You can tell they are good by the way they look at you, and they, not like Daddy, can tell what's wrong from the other side of the room, whereas Daddy pushes nasty old spoons and things down your throat and hurts you.

I once tried to syringe my wife's ears – never again. It was nearly the end of our marriage. She now goes off to the local hospital casualty department. I can't say that I was delighted when she developed an ear infection after one of her treatments, but I was very matter-of-fact when I cleared up the residue of the resulting damage.

Over the years, my family's lack of confidence has slowly undermined my own. Not only do they think I can't treat them and know nothing but I am beginning to feel it myself. So, whenever one of my children is ill, we usually describe the symptoms briefly to the postman, who has some experience of first-aid, and he outlines the general principles of treatment needed.

My greatest hurt was when one night, preparing a lecture into a tape recorder on the treatment of child complaints, my wife, who had heard every word that I was saying in the next room, came out and said, 'Isn't it terrible? Every woman reading or hearing that talk will think how lucky the wife of that doctor must be to have such an understanding man about the house, to know exactly what to do when the children are ill, or when they have behaviour troubles. And it's not like that at all.'

I did manage for a time to strike a working arrangement with a colleague in which we looked after each other's families, but the two lots of children got together at school and soon explained to each other the terrible dangers they were being exposed to.

The only time I ever appear popular in my line of treatment at home is when I decide someone is unfit to go to school – then I am the best doctor in the world. In spite of this my younger son gave me the *Seaman's Manual of Good Health* for Christmas. It is a book designed to keep you in perfect health if the nearest doctor is a thousand miles away.

In the children's view I am of some use elaborating on 'Dr Finlay's Casebook' or 'Emergency Ward 10', but must never ever criticise 'Dr Kildare'.

My major triumph was when I spotted that our dog hadn't got colic, but had started to go into labour after an unnoticed pregnancy. 'Gosh, Dad!' the family chorused. 'You really ought to have been a vet!'

9. First-Aid Examination

Taking examinations for the Red Cross and St John first-aid certificates I recognise as part of my duties as a general practitioner. It is usually hard work; however, I relate this to the hard work of the industrious members of the community who try and equip themselves to cope with minor and major accidents to their fellow beings.

So when I was asked by my partner to help him in examining the proficiency of the employees of an organisation I supposed was either a large florist's or grocer's, I reconciled myself to a strenuous afternoon's work for little reward.

We arrived at the very sophisticated office of the body who had invited us and I realised I had been mis-informed. We were actually examining members of the staff of the Intervention Board. I had never heard of it before, but apparently this is the body that guards our interests in the to-ing and fro-ing of agricultural prod-ucts in the Common Market.

By and large, people who are examined for first-aid certificates are fairly homely, community-minded people; it was somewhat surprising therefore to have a succession of highly intelligent honours graduates of varying degrees of sophistication to scrutinise.

My partner decided we would split up the task. He would start with the practical examinations, leaving the theory to me. The idea was that we would change over to break up the monotony of the afternoon.

As the afternoon wore on, the examinees became easier on the eye and more sophisticated. I noticed that any girl who arrived in knee-length boots and a short skirt was asked immediately by my partner to demon-strate the coma position (this means lying elegantly on one side with one knee drawn up – and it was usually a nylon encased knee followed by a leather boot).

This seemed to be about the only procedure he was covering and he seemed to be taking rather a long time over it. I was beginning to get worried about him. When I suggested that it was time we changed over, he confessed that he was quite happy to carry on with the practical side if I could cope with the theory.

Whereas he was enjoying a succession of beautiful girls, who would have held their own in a Miss World competition, twisting on the floor in front of him, I was left with the mundane task of asking them how they would remove foreign bodies from ears. And what they would do if they ruptured a varicose vein. (Not that any of these gorgeous creatures would consider having one!)

The climax of the afternoon was reached when my partner, as had become the habit, had an absolute dish luxuriously stretching in the coma position on the floor. Worried that he might kneel down and start personal mouth-to-mouth resuscitation on her, which was the only other practical procedure he was testing, I neglected to look at my next candidate for the oral examination.

I turned round to find the most gorgeous redhead looking me straight in the eye. I had not realised before how attractive I was.

'Excuse me,' she said, 'aren't you Dr Clifford who used to be in practice in Pembroke?'

I found that this was an ex-patient of mine, now twenty-six, who could not have matured better if I had instructed her myself – with an honours degree in zoology behind her, and all the essential parts of womanhood in front of her.

I realised I had started treating her when she was eight and I became aware how old I must be now, seeing the full-blooded woman she had grown into. We were soon lost in the reminiscences of practice days in Pembroke; her Uncle Ned was our gardener, and all thought of first aid soon slipped away.

My partner had still got his recumbent dish on the floor and seemed quite happy not to disturb the proceedings. At this stage one of the more senior members of the Intervention Board intervened. The tactful way it was done could only augur well for our Common Market prospects.

'Doctor,' she said, coughing, 'there are seventeen more candidates still to see.'

Reluctantly we tore ourselves away from our absorbing candidates and carried on with the work of the afternoon. We passed everyone. How could we possibly fail them?

And, in future, whenever I am called to assist in these examinations, which have previously been rather onerous, I shall go with a much lighter heart. Who knows, perhaps even Raquel Welch might decide she wants a certificate.

10. Psst! Read Any Good Books Lately? (1974)

There are many disadvantages, and a few advantages, arising from fuel crises – one of the mixed blessings being the cessation of television at the early hour of 10.30 p.m.

Being a television addict and prepared to watch anything at any time, however good or bad, I was suddenly left with a couple of extra hours on my hands. What better use could I put this bonus of unexpected time to than studying the *British Medical Journal*, much neglected by me in the past! Some of my more conscientious fellow general practitioners put one evening a week aside to study this authoritative journal – alas, I only dive into it occasionally, and most often to look at 'Jobs Abroad', when I feel that the pressures of general practice are beginning to overwhelm me.

Now I had the opportunity of enriching my mind and presenting my patients with a more knowledgeable, up-to-date and well-read practitioner.

Being thrifty I do not throw old books away, so I have a pile of journals to skip through in the enrichment process.

I see that I can ponder over an article describing 'Luteinising Hormone and Follicle Stimulating Hormone-Releasing Hypothalamic Pituitary-Gonadal Dysfunction'.

In this very same issue, I can be right up-to-date with a double-blind cross-over 'Study of Ketoprofen and Ibuprofen in the Management of Rheumatoid Arthritis', and, yippee, consider in the same week the relevance of 'Antigenicity of Candida Albicans Growth Phases to Diagnosis of Systemic Candidiasis', with a rearguard article on 'Severe Yersinia Pseudotuberculosis Infection Diagnosed at Laparoscopy'. As a cynic might say, 'Yersinia it all before.'

On a more cheerful note, the lighter side of this particular week includes 'Single-dose Treatment of Gonorrhoea', 'Scotland's Drink Problem' and 'Sjogren's Syndrome', and under 'News and Notes' I find 'Vibrio Food-poisoning on an Aeroplane', 'Compensation and Catastrophe', 'Labour Party Health Plans'.

I must point out that 'Compensation and Catastrophe' is quite a different article from 'Labour Party Health Plans', at least in this particular issue.

Having finished the front page and resisted the tantalising advertisements on the back page, particularly for those jobs with oil refineries, I venture to look around the middle pages which outline these fascinating titles. It is all too much for me. I can't understand it. So now, instead of being fresh with the most up-to-date knowledge, I have to return to my patients with the shattered feelings of my own incompetence and inability to be up-to-date with present treatments.

Perhaps this was just a bad week. Let's take another dip from the pile. Ah! This is more my cup of tea: 'Area Differences in Spontaneous Abortion Rates in South

Wales and Their Relation to Neural Tube Defect Incidence'.

I did hire a cottage in South Wales last Easter, but never saw anybody aborting anywhere, and didn't even have a chance to ask if anybody had a neural tube defect.

But, listen, 'Sonar Measurement of Fetal Crown-Rump Length as Means of Assessing Maturity in First Trimester of Pregnancy', and at last something I really do understand, 'Mechel's Diverticulum Presenting as Fistula-in-Ano'.

From my rugby-playing days this rings a bell, as in a certain song about a famous ball the village magician made a magic pass and obviously it was his Mechel's diverticulum that he disappeared up as opposed to the harsher words of that particular rhapsody.

Going back to the fuel shortages, I expect I could offer to work down the coal mines but, likely as not, they would put me on the night shift and I would still miss the late night film.

11. Where Do Elephants Go to Die?

9 had picked out the spot where I wished to be taken if I was ever ill. It was a cottage high on the cliff overlooking the sea, with the most magnificent view. That my friend who owns it is a cordon bleu cook is just by the way. I know there is a plug for the TV in the room because I have seen it. In the tender balm of these surroundings, although perhaps I wouldn't be in too great a hurry to get well, I would without a doubt thoroughly enjoy the particular malady I was suffering from. The last place I ever wanted to be ill in was a hospital, as the experience of friends has convinced me that the whole hospital routine is designed not only to prevent you from enjoying your illness, but by applying such a vigorous routine you are actually trying to get better quickly to get back to your home comforts.

Fortune would have it that being unwell, after some investigations I was ordered into hospital. I have few indulgences, but I do like a Havana cigar before breakfast – it settles me and I can start the day tranquil and relaxed.

But on my first morning, lighting my expensive dummy with my morning tea, which they had insisted on bringing at 5.30 a.m., had the same effect as letting off an incendiary bomb. Sisters and nurses rushed with fire extinguishers from all directions, and my poor cigar was snatched from my mouth. I was deprived of this necessity for a whole two weeks just because the man in the next bed was in an oxygen tent – and, ugh!, tea at 5.30 a.m. The only time previously I had had tea at this hour was when I was driving all day to the Motor Show, and then I had to spend two days in bed afterwards recovering.

I thought there must be some exciting reason for having been got up so early, but the next thing was at 6 o'clock when they brought round chipped enamel bowls to wash and shave in, and a red-coloured liquid to gargle with. By now I did see a little method in their madness. Here was I, at six in the morning, washed, shaved, sharpened by being deprived of my cigar, but really on my toes, hungry and raring to go.

There seemed little action after the wash, so calling over the least belligerent-looking staff nurse, I enquired of the form.

'Oh,' she said, 'you can now go to sleep till breakfast at eight.'

Sleep now? This was obviously some form of subtle brain-washing. They could waken me during the night, wash me, whet my appetite with a cup of tea and then tell me to go to sleep again.

With my gastric juices now welling in my throat, I managed to pass the next two hours frantically doing the crossword puzzles in the two evening papers I had brought with me.

At 8 o'clock, with a bustle and change of staff, in

comes breakfast on a steaming metal trolley. Porridge (which I hadn't had since I was at school, but which now I wouldn't have swopped for caviar), and sausages and bacon. I watched the trolley come slowly down the ward, and I have never seen two little blackened objects and a slab of bacon look so delicious. The trolley seemed to take years as it crept towards me, but at last it did reach me and a plate of this tempting repast was put in front of me. As I reached forward to take my first mouthful, the tray was suddenly whipped from me by a grey-haired sister, who was followed by a nurse carrying a sinister-looking metal tray.

'No breakfast for you,' she snapped. 'You're for a gastric test meal.'

The nurse dropped the metal tray in the place of my breakfast one, and quick as a flash started to push a rubber tube up my nose, shouting 'swallow'.

At this stage I decided that even if I dropped dead on the way out, from now on I was going to get better quickly. The nurse kept pushing this endless tube up my nose and wasn't satisfied until I had swallowed two yards of it. 'What about breakfast?' I croaked.

'You'll have a glass of glucose water at 9 a.m.,' she replied and whisked herself away.

I like a glass of brandy in the evening, I always enjoy a cup of coffee, and nobody appreciates a glass of wine with a meal more than I do, but a glass of glucose water at 9 a.m. is no substitute for any of these. For the rest of the morning at hourly intervals people kept coming and sucking up the contents of my stomach through the tube in my nose and taking it away in bottles.

This was a gross invasion of my privacy. I have always got on well with my stomach – I have never enquired what it did, and my stomach in its turn never bothered

44

what I did, unless the mixture I threw into it was too rich, and then it protested in its own unmistakable way. Now its ghastly secrets were being exposed in front of me in bottles. It was all so unfair.

All morning during my hourly syphonings, my only distraction was the ward traffic, which was a close second to Piccadilly Circus. Trolleys coming and going, men waving to their chums as they went off to have their hernia or appendix done, like men leaving for the front-line, returning an hour later ashen and unconscious as if they had been victims of the first poisonous gas attack.

By 3 o'clock when visitors came, tired through lack of sleep, weak with hunger, I thought I had been in hospital for three months. By the attitude of my friends, the firm squeeze of the shoulder without speaking and the way they ate my grapes ('They will be no use to him'), I knew I must have looked pretty ill. Eventually they went and, looking at my watch, I saw it was now 4 p.m. As I usually go to bed at twelve there were still eight hours of the day left.

They removed my tubes and at 4.30 I was given some tea and a piece of cake. Things had begun to improve. I felt the surge of strength with my nutrient and began to take a more active interest in what was going on. I did my hair and took stock of the nurses. Gosh! That blonde one would grace any party.

I could just imagine her in a low-cut evening dress.

I spent the next hour trying to catch her eye. She was obviously playing hard to get. But at last she came smiling towards me, with a little black book in her hand. Boy, what a figure; she was obviously going to date me. A beautiful smile crept across her face, she opened her book and said, 'Tell me, have you opened your bowels today?'

This was the end.

I slowly settled down to the routine of the ward. Eventually it did seem that a lot of the things that were done made sense.

I found I was with twenty-six of the most interesting men I had ever met in my life. We swopped magazines, operation stories, and a camaraderie grew up; this was the best ward in the best hospital ever.

The nurses worked a full day at full tilt, having to do the most distasteful things without flinching, yet had time to be kind and talk to us.

People round me seemed to be getting better and it was with some emotion that we said goodbye to the repaired bodies going back on to the road again. In my last week I was up and helped with the food trolley, and on the last two days I was allowed to boil the eggs for tea.

When I was pronounced fit I hated going. I had to leave warm comradeship and comfort, and go out into the world on my own again.

I think if I watched a sea view for too long I would be bored, and I might even tire of my friend's cooking.

Yes, there is no doubt, the next time I'm ill, hospital is definitely the place for me.

Deep Thoughts

12. The Three Wise Men

As I grow older one of the things that I regret most is that time has taken its toll of wiser, older people whose friendships I have valued.

Three I have missed more than any. Firstly, my senior partner when I first went into practice. He was the most unselfish man and certainly the best and most caring doctor I have known.

Secondly, a wise old bookseller with whom I shared many philosophical cups of tea, and who had fewer prejudices than anyone I have known.

Thirdly, Herbert Hodge, the taxi driver/author. He was the most honest writer I have known. He could not repeat himself. Everything he wrote had to be new and original. He eventually burnt himself out striving for honest perfection.

These three men I miss badly; they were a very important part of my life.

During one of the periodic crises that we have in this country, I asked my senior partner what was the answer to these problems of violence in the community, industrial

unrest, political upheavals, international incidents, and
even war itself. Surely there must be some way of
preventing this? Was government from the left or the
right, or even the centre, the solution; should they act
together, or was there no solution?

My partner said, 'I think the answer to society's
problem is simple.

'However good a system is, unless the people who
make up that system are good enough the system won't
work. If, on the other hand, you have good enough
people, whatever system you place them in will work
because of the quality of the people in it.

'We don't need better government or better management, we just need better people.

'I believe,' he said, 'that if individuals could form a
habit of making a conscious effort to do at least one
unselfish act a day, society would have few problems.'

I discussed my partner's thoughts with the practical,
honest Herbert. He agreed and considered all the ways
in which you could start people forming this habit.

Herbert worried that people would try to turn it into
a sect, or start applying rules. 'It would have to be kept
basically simple,' he said. 'There would have to be some
of us passing on the idea of this daily unselfish act, yet
doing it without meetings or gatherings. It would have
to be something individual and personal, and yet on the
other hand, public.' He thought that we would have to
find some small sign that people could wear so that in a
crowded train or restaurant, or at work, they could be
comforted by looking round and seeing a great number
of other people in their immediate vicinity who'd made
an open declaration of at least trying to do one unselfish
act a day for their fellow men.

So Herbert suggested that if you dipped the head of

a pin in a yellow gloss paint, let it dry, and then stuck it into the edge of your lapel, you'd have a small unostentatious sign showing that you had made a commitment. There should be no communion or discussion with like people who were trying to take this same course of action, it should be kept basically simple.

He suggested the idea could be spread in the same way as a chain letter: you gave a yellow pin to two people, explaining the idea and the commitment, instructing each of the recipients to repeat the process, giving two more pins to two other people, and so on.

My friend, the bookseller, agreed with my partner's formula. His suggestion for distribution was that you should award yellow pins to anyone you saw doing some obvious unselfish act, hoping that they would repeat the process when they benefited from someone else's unselfishness.

We discussed this project. As with many other ideas about so many other things, in the end it was put on one side and we moved on to explore other ideas and other philosophies.

I have always remembered these three wise men who, towards the end of long, interesting and relatively unselfish lives, felt that they had an answer to society's problems.

As I look round today I wonder if society has finally completely lost its head. We have countries of the same ideology tearing at each other's throats; we have men in different branches of the same religion killing each other in the name of God. Society becomes more violent, the streets become progressively unsafe, football matches are often just used as battle grounds, and man's inhumanity to man increases.

Who is responsible for this situation?

I do not think we can blame governments or the police or employers or the Church or trade unions. The blame must lie squarely upon all our shoulders. We are just not nice enough or good enough people.

The solution lies not with any power group, but with the single individual – you and me.

My three wise men believed that the answer was so simple – all we had to do was each day, each one of us, make a conscious effort to do one unselfish act. Although my three wise men never sorted out between them how to initiate this scheme, they did all agree that a yellow-headed pin stuck in the lapel could be the sign that you were willing to have a go.

I'm going to stick one in mine. Who knows?

13. Poor Sonia Blatchingthorpe

For two mornings Sonia Blatchingthorpe had noticed traces of blood in her stool. She was sufficient of a realist to know that this meant either a complete readjustment or the end of her career.

For five years now, her fine contralto tones had dominated the music world. She would always command a packed audience in any of the world's leading music houses. Her achievements had only been possible through thirty-six years of complete devotion to her art.

Her pure, clear 'flatal' tone had first been recognised by an elderly aunt when she was only three months old. She was straight away transferred to one of the national musical nurseries, where she amazed everyone by her forwardness, particularly her control. It is said that she never soiled a nappy after she was four and a half months, but there is no evidence to prove this.

Having started training almost from birth, a life of low-residue diets and split-second bowel actions were little hardship to her.

She accepted the harsh rigours of the National

Training School with a selfless devotion that eventually took her to the top of her profession.

It meant years of hard work with at first little reward, although for two years running she won the junior medal for clearness of tone.

She was always at the top of her class. At thirteen she was being talked of as a future star, and at sixteen she was already beginning to take minor lead parts. To some extent the war held her back, as there was a limited number of concerts and no opportunities to study abroad. But like the rest of the best of the company, she was wisely kept by the government in a place of safety, so that even if there had been wholesale destruction, this art at least would have survived. They were all given priority foodstuffs, and during the whole six years were able to stick to their 'flatist's' diet.

It was probably due to this governmental foresight that in the immediate post-war period we led the world. I feel that even if she had not been able to take advantage of these privileges, she still had the natural talent to rise to the top.

Jack Gater, the noted critic, once likened her top 'flatus' to the crack of doom.

She was loved by the common people in the galleries, who always cried for more and yet more of her rich tones.

She was fortunate in her career that she never contracted dysentery or colitis as did many of her colleagues, for these are two of the scourges of the profession.

She was in Milan when Gutupsey, the famous Italian tenor, inadvertently drank cabbage water before a performance, was incontinent on the stage, and subsequently shot himself.

Apart from the quality of her 'flati', Sonia had a beautiful pair of lean buttocks, which she took care of, and which were a pleasure to behold in their own right.

She had once, in her twenties, nearly married into the peerage, but Lord X had been adamant that he wanted an heir, and knowing how pregnancy weakened the muscles of the perineum, Sonia had eventually turned him down and devoted herself even more deeply to her chosen career.

Now, the blood in the toilet pan could mean only one thing: haemorrhoids.

Some people had gone back to work after haemorrhoidectomies, but only to take low bass parts, and it had taken them painful months of learning their art again.

Sonia looked back over her years of dedication. Years of the strictest training and discipline. Years without being able to eat as other people. No family life or the pursuance of selfish hobbies and pleasure. No proper holidays. No real friends. No real relaxation. Her art had meant more to her than all this, and had been her life.

She thought of the pleasure her 'flati' had given to countless millions, and had carried her to the supreme pinnacle of world champion 'flatist' for tone and range. She was without a doubt, until this ensuing disability, at the very top of the tree.

She was now faced with the ignominy of retirement with everybody knowing why, or the painful business of having her piles cut out and trying to reshape her life in some other key.

She thought it all over very carefully, then jumped into the river and was drowned.

14. Soliloquy at Evening Surgery

Ever since my father taught me, when being over-whelmed by someone's personability, to steady myself and imagine them sitting on the toilet, I have felt that I am at least the equal of any of my fellow men.

As I earn my living in medicine and general practice, where I am condemned to spend the best part of my life with people who have, either literally or metaphorically, got their trousers down, I feel there is little hope for me.

I have arrived at some formula for survival by managing to train myself always to keep one-third – and even, sometimes, two-thirds – of my mind looking out of the window.

When a fat and pompous patient is laying down the law or giving judgment, or taking part in some dignified pageantry, I wonder how he ever gets a proper look at his feet or completes his toilet. In contrast, when I am injecting the piles of an artist, be he writer, painter or singer, I think of the joy of his art, not of the particular job I have in hand.

I have not yet been able to make a compromise

between these two extremes.

During the time I have been occupying myself with these procedures and processes, the saved one-third of my mind has been busy in my garden, mending my fishing net, making a golf shot, or even composing a speech for the Rotary dinner.

People come for advice, for some magic formula to solve all problems. They come because they want to be told what to do. They want the answer. I don't know it; nobody knows it; there is no answer. They come lacking direction and all I can do is to point them in some direction. It may not be the direction in which they want to go, but any is better than none and, hopefully, they will have found a direction of their own once they are on the move again.

I have no authority, no wisdom, no sincerity. I reach into the depths of my energy, doling out handfuls of my own substance in an effort to keep people on the move. They stream in. I am an insincere Solomon. I realise that the limit of my achievement is to assist some individuals over a stile, knowing that my help will only last until the next stile, hoping they will be able to get over, unaided, when they reach it.

I cannot swim around the great lake of life supporting people in the water. All I am able to do is to throw lifebelts to some who look as if they might drown.

There are some days when I know all there is to know, but most days I know nothing at all. I can recognise quality but am too inarticulate to name it. I believe that hard work is like salt and, without it, everything loses flavour.

As I spend my time looking after people's ills, my company is only sought by the unwell and my reserves are almost always near to exhaustion. If someone is managing, achieving and being successful, by definition he doesn't seek my company or my help. I seem to live in a half-world in a half-light, populated by inadequate and hopeless people, without talent, without quality and without any justifiable reason for carrying on. Yet, through the sneer in which I am writing, and because I am getting it down on paper, I am naming the villain; my tension and depression start to be relieved. I begin to recognise in the people I have been observing goodness and other qualities, and they rise in stature before me.

Slowly I return to my equilibrium as, by stepping on the jumble of what I have written, which was the steam of a tiring and sapping day, I have risen a plane and see the beauty and purpose of all things and all people and leave the excreta of my mind behind.

Courage

15. Ben Fellowes

The first time that I was able to recognise sheer courage was when we found that Ben Fellowes had an inoperable growth.

As far as I knew, Ben had led an unobtrusive life. He was the village upholsterer. I don't think that he was an easy man to work with, but I don't think he was a terribly difficult one either.

He accepted hospital life with the aplomb of a countryman, soon settling down to the routine of the ward. He had left things very late before seeking medical advice, and after some investigations it was found that he was far too advanced to be given any help.

Ben somehow got someone to tell him that not only could nothing be done, but also he had at the most six months to live. He must have wheedled it out on the pretext of putting his affairs in order, as I know that it is not the general policy to divulge this.

When people ask if they are going to die, they only ask to be told they are not. I also do not accept that a point of hopelessness is ever reached in modern-day medicine, as new cures are found every day and outlooks or certain diseases change overnight.

Past experience has shown me that to be certain of the cause of a disease is to be sometimes wrong; and I do know, if you take away a man's hope completely you immediately cut down the amount of time he has left with us.

With this in mind I sent Ben to a deep-ray specialist with a covering note saying that here was a man without any hope and could they possibly do something for him. But again Ben must have done or said something as back he came with a note saying nothing could in fact be done. This time he even managed to get somebody to tell him that he wouldn't live more than three months.

Throughout all this Ben had shown no obvious sign of emotion. He conducted himself in a businesslike manner, putting his affairs in order. He would discuss his coming death openly and unaffectedly. He fixed up his shop lease, settled his outstanding accounts and gave me two coronation five-shilling pieces for my little boys for all the trouble I had taken.

In the first month of the three, Ben went off by train to see and say goodbye to friends, explaining that perhaps he wouldn't be able to get around too well later. He then came back to stay with his son, travelling round with the firm's van or sitting quietly in it by himself behind the row of houses where his son lived, enjoying the last fine days of the summer.

I never remember him complaining, and as far as I know he had no faith, creed or philosophy to sustain him. He was always pleased and grateful when I went to see him and never requested anything more than codeine tablets to relieve whatever anguish he was suffering. He got progressively weaker, and died quietly exactly three months later as predicted.

I only knew him in this last phase of his life, but I have always felt that he was one of those few men who, spurning hope, had the rare courage to stand squarely up to things as they are. When he knew the problem without adornments, he said to himself: 'the only thing I have left to do is to die. I shall make the best job of it I can.'

16. The Available Gentleman

Herbert Barlow lived alone in a room at the top of the large house in which my wife and I had a flat when we were first married.

He claimed to be a gentleman, a writer and a man of the theatre, and he was without a doubt the most available man I have ever known. Meeting him for the first time confirmed most of his claims.

He looked like a writer: a stern, dignified face, carefully groomed silver hair, and a deep resonant voice that trotted out theatre platitudes, punctuated with growling 'my dears'. He had a perfect set of teeth.

He looked, and was, a man acting a part, and through all the time we knew him we fluctuated from thinking that he was a complete sham to joining in with him and saying the right words and lines. He lived frugally, explaining that when his last marriage broke up he decided to dispense with possessions, leaving himself free to dash off to the south of France, New York or Italy if anybody required him.

He said, 'I don't have any dependants now and I don't

intend to be dependent on anybody else.'

There was no doubt that he did write, for in his little room there were five fully prepared manuscripts of plays on his desk. 'Once I get a couple of these on in the West End I shall be made – look at dear old Maugham,' (Herbert considered Maugham an intimate and an equal), 'he had exactly the same trouble and finally had five plays on at the same time.'

These plays were always nearly being produced; Herbert would say, 'Dear old A is interested,' naming a household name in the theatre, and I would pretend to believe this, until one day when I was with him in his room, the phone did ring, and there was old A asking for Herbert and obviously knowing him – but somehow his play never got produced. I did see that they were nearly produced by people who mattered, and who knew Herbert well.

In all, I knew Herbert over ten years, in which time he wrote twelve plays. His manuscripts, beautifully prepared, could not be bettered; they included intricate stage directions, and for some of them he built elaborate model stage sets.

I read them all. By the very businesslike way they had been presented they should have been produced. Picking up the manuscript and folder one knew immediately, as when one first met Herbert, that these were professional plays, written by a professional and a man of the theatre, but on reading them they seemed to be all dialogue and manuscript, stage directions, and details about lights and props; there was no story, no characters emerging, and I could never understand what he had been trying to say. That is until after Herbert had explained them all to me himself.

Herbert used to talk of his days before the war, in the

south of France – 'My natural home, Old Boy.' He was
then a film scriptwriter and living on half the income he
was receiving – 'Went there to die, Old Boy. My dear
friend Dr X, who is now a medical superintendent at the
Great Y Hospital, said I had consumption, coughing up
blood, thought I had only six months to live.'

This was the typical, hackneyed, classic melodrama
around which all the episodes of Herbert's life seemed
to evolve. 'One of the biggest disappointments of my life
at that time,' he said, 'was Gertie, half of a famous
dancing sisters act. We had been living together for
eight years. As soon as she knew I was ill, she left me.
Eventually she married Lord Z.' Anyone connected
with Herbert couldn't possibly have married into anything less than the peerage.

'Do you see your friend the doctor at all now?' I said.

'No, Old Boy, haven't seen him for years. He married
again and I just couldn't get on with his wife. If I was
ever ill, though, I would of course go straight to him.'

All the important people Herbert knew were just out
of reach. They were intimates, but there was always
some reason why they should never be in touch with
him; either they brought back old memories, or there
was some friction such as a new wife, or he didn't want
to get in touch with them until he was once more
re-established in the theatre.

'Of course,' he said, 'the war finished my stay in the
south of France; had to come back to England.'

Now it would have been typical of Herbert to say that
the government had sent a battleship to rescue him from
under a hail of enemy fire, or that he had at least swum
from Dunkirk, but he never gave an account of the
circumstances of his return.

What was certain was that, at the beginning of the

war, he was the manager of a large London theatre. He talked about the royalty he entertained there, about the private film shows for the prime minister, and how he was on intimate terms with them. Coupled with these stories of his association with these great men, and his theatre and writing achievements, were his stories of daily triumphs in the local market where he had got a penny off coffee, twopence off cheese, or found a remnant of material from which he could make a shirt.

He had bought an old sewing machine for £2, and could make any type of apparel. He made me a shirt, and an evening dress for my wife.

I am sure that sometimes he went hungry. He had no visible means of support, other than from some occasional play-doctoring for ambiguous theatre companies. 'Plenty of money backing this, Old Boy,' he would say. 'They have asked me to make something of it.' I saw two of these plays.

Having his manuscripts typed out cost money. Posting them cost money. He said, 'I have a couple of hundred pounds capital, Old Boy, but don't like to touch it.' I was never able to bring myself to believe this.

He claimed to have stage-managed sometime or other every London theatre, starting after the First World War at the old Alhambra Theatre with 'Bing Boys on Broadway' and the Dalgleith Ballet.

Herbert tucked himself away in this top room with his memories, his manuscripts and his great associations. 'My biggest mistake, Old Boy,' he said, 'was leaving the West End.' He explained the break-up of his domestic life, which led him to his present circumstances.

He had had a long and varied marital life, which I never knew in detail. Association with the opposite sex no longer featured on any of his programmes. Life was as simple as possible. In his room he had a bed, a desk, two armchairs and a double gas ring. He came down to our flat for his weekly bath. He had a devoted daily called Elsie, who came and 'did' for him for nothing. She adored him and always thought of him as a great man.

He had so arranged his domestic pattern that he was ready at a moment's notice if required by a theatre or film company. 'I could pack and be off for six months tomorrow if they needed me, Old Boy,' he would say. He even didn't like being out of the district in case he missed the call that he knew one day would come – the call that would lead to the success which so far had eluded him.

He spent the last two years of his life fighting a terminal illness that would have finished most people in six months. During that time he wrote a spiritual play that was to be the climax of his life.

He finished his play and sent it round, and it had the usual rejection slips. Nobody was interested because, although he had been a very good stage manager and could change other peoples' manuscripts, he just couldn't write plays himself.

As he was getting progressively weaker I took it upon myself to get in touch with his great friend Dr X, superintendent of the Great Y Hospital, and to my surprise Dr X was a great friend and took him straight into his own hospital, giving him full VIP treatment.

His health was failing so rapidly that I knew he would never attend another first night. Unbeknown to him I contacted some of the great men of the theatre he had mentioned, explained the situation and the importance of Herbert's last play. Again to my surprise, they not only knew him but also had a great affection for him. He had been a successful film scriptwriter and well-known stage manager.

We got together, and one of the more important celebrities wrote to Herbert saying how much he liked this last play and that he hoped to produce it at an indefinite date in the future – a date when we all knew that Herbert would no longer be there to help with the directions of the set.

Herbert accepted this letter. 'I knew, Old Boy,' he said, 'that there was a purpose in my struggling on these last two years. I know this play has a message,' and his eyes shone with triumph through his gaunt face.

Herbert died with dignity, as I knew he would. I contacted what relatives I could find and, having perhaps been closer to him than anyone else, offered to help pay the funeral expenses. But Herbert had left £200 in the bank – enough for all the expenses, and some left over for Elsie, who had worked for him for nothing for so many years.

On my desk in my study I keep a pile of beautifully prepared play manuscripts in a cardboard folder, tied round with a piece of brown ribbon. Nobody will ever produce them, but they are my memorial to my great friend, Herbert Barlow – Gentleman, Writer and Man of the Theatre. A man who always kept himself available, never realising that he had spent so much of his life pretending to be the sort of person he actually was.

17. Television Set

My old friend Miss Oke lived for forty-seven
years in a small room that looked out on the main
road to the sea in the westward part of my practice.

She had not left her bed during this time, and it was
mainly due to the devotion of her life-long friend,
companion and nurse, Miss Lord, with whom she
shared her room, that she had lived happily for so long.

One would think that two ladies who had to live so
long in such narrow surroundings would have led a
small, insular life. Far from this, they had a wide circle
of friends, and a much wider circle with whom they
corresponded.

My problem was seeing that they didn't get too over-
tired by having too many visitors.

Miss Oke once said to me, 'The difficulty is, Doctor,
that so many people come to see me because they think
I have time to listen.' Both Miss Oke and Miss Lord
were practising Christians and could be said to enjoy
their religion.

They enjoyed selected radio programmes and, for

several years, had a small robin as a daily visitor, who came and ate his meals from a saucer by Miss Oke's bed.

Round about Miss Oke's eighty-third birthday, a charitable organisation in the town asked if they would like a television set. I wasn't too happy about this; these two ladies had become successfully adjusted to their environment, and now the world – a very different world to the one they remembered – was going to be brought to their bedside. This could easily upset the whole pattern to which they were so well adjusted.

I wondered what their reaction would be if the first programme they saw was a modern play or a cowboy film.

My first visit after delivery of the set dispelled all my fears. I was met by two beaming faces, and Miss Oke said, 'Doctor, do you know that for the first time for fifty years, I have actually taken part in a church service?'

Television was a tremendous success. Sunday with its church services and community hymn singing was their best day, and Miss Oke was quite certain that on one Sunday the bishop had nodded to her during the service. Any programme about the royal family and people of title came next on their list.

Their television took them round castles and cathedrals, introduced them to people of every creed and colour, and showed them countries and continents as if they were seasoned world travellers. The world they had read and heard about for five decades was suddenly brought into their own little world of four walls and a window. It never disappointed them, and by some sort of natural selection they never appeared to have tuned into a programme that was objectionable to them.

Miss Oke, whose health had for many years been

71

pretty poor, died five months after she had received her television set.

I last saw her two days before her death. She lay in bed, her eyes shining and bright, and said, 'We have just seen the most exciting finish to the Lords test match, and now I am sitting in the front row at Wimbledon watching the tennis.' Life had never been fuller for her.

I shall always remember Miss Oke and Miss Lord. It is unlikely that I shall ever meet anybody quite like them again.

Their physical handicaps had not prevented them from making a success of life. I shall remember them particularly when I turn on my television set, as it was this wonderful invention that made the last chapter of an eighty-year-long life the fullest; it allowed a fine old lady who had been confined to bed for forty-seven years to get up from it, and join in with us for the last few months before she finally left us.

Travel and Adventure

18. Vive le Rugby!

Watching England meet France at Twickenham this season brought back vividly the time when I was a medical student and I went on my first French rugby tour. I look back upon it as one of the highlights of my life.

We assembled at Victoria Station the day after a very hectic Cornish tour, having played three games in three days, to set off for France – boat and train to Paris, spend a night there, then by train to three games in the Rhone Valley area, train back, a night in Paris and back to London. This sounded marvellous. We were to play two of the best French teams, but looking at the motley crowd collecting, I did just wonder about our prospects. Examinations, injuries and the Cornish tour deprived our hospital side of most of its stars. To make our numbers up to twenty-five, which the French had so generously invited, urgent calls went out the night before, and even then we only just managed to muster our complement.

Anybody who was free for a few days could come.

There was the jovial captain of the B XV, the club's society secretary who had never really played rugger but arranged the rugby dance on which the club finances depended, and one or two other hangers-on from the extra A team and the schools XV.

There was one character whom I could never place. I assumed he must be somebody's relative. I don't know now whether he was a rugby player at all, for he claimed to be the trainee manager of the Savoy Hotel.

We had a calm crossing, arriving in Paris with a night in front of us before travelling on to Lyons. Our Parisian night in no way freshened us for our coming ordeal. We de-trained at a place called Tarrare, near Lyons, in the middle of the afternoon, then were whisked off to a very nice hotel, and had a champagne reception and dance.

We were the first English side to play in that area since the war, and they really did their utmost with their hospitality.

We were playing a local representative side the next day, and everyone assured us how easy the game would be. We were the equivalent of a first division soccer team playing one of the southern league clubs.

The following morning there was a civic reception. We were taken round a silk factory, wined and, then about an hour before we played, given more champagne. We played on a sun-baked pitch in the evening against this local enthusiastic side. We had not put our strongest team out (although I am not sure what our strongest side was). If we had played all twenty-five of the party I doubt if it would have been as good as our normal team with all us stars available.

It was an impressive start. The French kicked off a high long kick for their forwards to follow up. Our full-back, the captain from the B XV, the most sociable chap, stood there like a rock waiting for the ball to be caught and safely disposed of. If he had been able to wear his glasses on the rugby field there is no doubt that he would have been a first class rugby player, but without them he was about as blind as a bat. He stood there, arms open, firmly fixed to the spot, the ball soared over his head, bouncing about twenty yards behind him, perfectly placed for a French forward to pick up and score their first try.

The French, then realising that our full-back was practically blind, exploited him for the rest of the game, and we lost 12-11. They nudged each other, saying, 'These English, they keep their cards up their sleeves. Wait till they play the big game tomorrow.'

That night they treated us to another dance and champagne party. The captain of the B XV, celebrating his 'success', sat at a table quietly on his own, surrounded with empty champagne bottles.

The next day we played Lyons at the Lyons Olympic Stadium. Before we started, a band of forty white-gauntleted *gendarmes* paraded round the pitch playing martial music. An immaculately turned-out French team trotted onto the pitch to the cheers of the crowd, and then we trotted on, and it was the first time I was able to take a look at us as a group from, shall I say, an aesthetic angle.

These were the days of clothes rationing, and rugby clothes were at the bottom of the list for coupons. Our kit was still wet and filthy from our Cornish tour, nobody had cleaned his boots and we really looked scruffy.

I was better dressed than most, because, as a spare shirt, I had taken an old dark-green one (we were playing in blue) that my grandfather used to wear for playing soccer – it had a lace-up neck into which I had laboriously sewn a semi-stiff collar.

We lost to Lyons 25-3, but we weren't disgraced. It is always policy when playing in France just to lose each game. You are then assured of a successful party afterwards.

We had a dinner in Lyons with the Lyons Club, which ended with our captain doing a naked Zulu dance on the table, during which he accidentally poured a glass of wine onto the head of Madame La France, the guest of honour, who had been the head of the Resistance for the area. She must have wondered whether her efforts to oust the Germans had been worthwhile when she found they were being replaced by naked 'Africans' pouring wine over her.

We had a scrum-down in the hall, smashing all the glasses then, drunken and singing, staggered to our bus, which was taking us to our next destination.

The bus journey was a nightmare. We had been playing rugby, drinking and travelling now for as long as I could remember; some were being sick, some were fighting, whilst the rest just shouted drunken abuse at one another.

We arrived at the next place where, instead of being put up at a hotel, we were being boarded out with families. There were rows of cars and pleasantly smiling French people welcoming their allies and liberators. We started to leave the bus, and the only term that could be used to describe us was to say that we spewed forth from it. Immediately most of the waiting hosts disappeared without taking anybody, leaving several of our party lying in the town square quite unconscious. Half of us, instead of sleeping the night in comfortable French beds, eventually finished up roughing it in a barn.

The next day, after one more civic reception, we were

to play this town's side, which had a very good reputation, and against whom the previous year the hospital side, with all stars present, had come back from 17-10 at half-time to win 20-17.

We were in pretty desperate straits, and agreed to play substitutes. This is about as un-British as one could get in rugby, but everyone of our party of twenty-five came onto the pitch at least once. Our trainee manager, who I think was really a trainee waiter, came on five different times in five different positions. The Captain of the B XV played in the forwards, where he didn't have to see the ball, and played much better. The social secretary came on as wing-forward in the first half and, after tripping everybody up and generally getting in the way, committed the worst crime at half-time; when throwing his orange peel off the field, he hit our only mobile three-quarter in the eye with it and disabled him for the rest of the game.

We had all taken glucose tablets to keep us going, but in spite of this were 30-0 down by half-time. The French, remembering the come-back of the year before, waited hopefully. In the second half, our glucose obviously began to work. We were up, we stormed the French and scored seven points in as many minutes. The crowd was on its feet. This was the stuff they wanted. But in a few minutes it had worn off and we were eventually beaten 45-7.

We played so badly that this town didn't invite another English team for five years.

By some booking mistake we had no seats back to Paris the next day, and all twenty-five of us had to stand crammed between the toilets of two railway coaches for eight hours. We spent another night in Paris and then staggered home.

It was five or six days later before many of us were able to struggle from our soft English beds, and nobody could give a clear account of our Continental excursion.

I went on several French rugby tours, but none ever reached the heights of my first.

19. The Eight Men from Niger

9 was employed as a doctor/Land Rover driver for a trans-Saharan safari company, and we were travelling what had become a routine circuit starting from the El Golea Oasis in Algeria, then via Tamanrasset, Agades and Bilma in Niger, back into Algeria to the Djanet Oasis and the foot of the Tassili plateau. One of the main objectives of the expedition was to climb up the Tassili plateau and spend some days exploring and photographing the prehistoric paintings that abound there.

We had had a good trip and our passengers, wealthy Americans, were nice people who joined in with the general chores; apart from one or two minor frictions, the tour had passed without any trouble.

Djanet is the nearest oasis to the Niger border and is separated from Libya by the Tassilil plateau. Our passengers had been due to fly out from here after spending five days on the plateau, but on arrival we found the airport shut. Then started the lengthy, complicated business of trying to find out when the next plane from the nearest place was, which eventually turned out to be Inanemas, some three hundred miles away.

There were five staff in our party: a leader, a camp-master driver, a mechanic driver, a cook and myself. The cook had sprained an ankle and couldn't climb, the mechanic had to see to the maintenance of the vehicles and the leader of the expedition was stuck trying to arrange to fly the Americans out so they wouldn't miss their connections back to New York. So it was left to me to lead the plateau exploration with John, the camp master, as my second in command.

It is not a tremendous physical feat to do the climb up the plateau and there are ropes to help negotiate the more difficult parts, but there is some fairly stiff going.

The night before our ascent, we had met two Swiss reporters who had asked to be included in our party as they were not properly equipped. This didn't lessen their baggage, though, and when we drove to the foot of the plateau our total party consisted of seven Americans, three of whom were women, two Englishmen, two Swiss, two guides, three donkey drivers and eight donkeys.

The climb up the plateau starts about ten miles outside the Djanet Oasis and the plateau itself is the nearest to the description of Conan Doyle's *Lost World* that I know. You climb up to 10,000 feet, and suddenly you come into a land of beautiful rock shapes, shrubs, grazing and water interspersed by flat stretches of broken rock terrain.

Before starting the slow climb we had the long process of loading the donkeys. The tiny Algerian donkey carries almost as much as a camel and has a very hard time with his heavy loads, scrambling up steep slopes, and coming down, slipping and sliding, the drivers taking little care of them.

Waiting near us at the foot of the climb were eight of the most scruffy, impoverished, undernourished men that I have ever seen. They had few possessions, their clothes were tattered rags and they looked exhausted and lost. I was busy organising and took little notice of them, but as we started to climb, they climbed also, just keeping ahead, following the track pointed out by our guides.

I, as the leader, climbed from the back to make our tourists feel comfortable, not hurrying them on as we had a couple of older people in the party, and I knew it was going to take them all their time to get to the top. We had a very cheerful little Algerian guide called Sherf and all seemed to be going well, with my party climbing much better than I had expected.

Climbing past me after the first hour on the way up was one of the party of eight who had got left behind. As he passed me he coughed and I could hear his coughing going up above me as he climbed on, catching up the rest of his party.

After he passed, I noticed patches of frothy red blood spattered on the track at regular intervals and I realised that they must be from this last climber.

I had climbed the plateau before, going up the steep paths, but this time our guides led us into a cleft of rocks and, before our amazed clients knew it, they were shinning up fixed ropes with tremendous overhangs that one dare not look down. In other circumstances I would have found myself very hard pressed to do this climb, not being a climber, with such heights and drops below, but being in charge I had to push on, encouraging the rest, and all of our clients behaved most creditably, getting up this quite difficult climb with the aid of ropes in not too long a time.

The eight natives who had joined us refused to risk the climb and instead had taken a long, tedious path round, pointed out by the guide.

We got way ahead of our donkeys, having climbed the cliffs, and on reaching the top of the plateau started to walk the first five miles to the base camp that we were setting up in an area called Tamrit. The flat terrain here gives way to tall avenues between rocks, and you find some of the cave paintings that were first described by the Frenchman Henry Lhote. There is also water and shelter.

Arriving at Tamrit, we sat down smoking and chatting, pleased with ourselves that we had overcome this quite arduous climb. Tamrit is by the main pathway that leads through these sand-sculptured structures and rough surfaces down into Chad, and struggling up the path we saw these eight men coming along slowly with our man at the back hawking and coughing up blood.

They sat down in a surly, unfriendly group while two of them went off to fill their battered goatskin with water. I went over to them with the guide and the Swiss, who took presents of cigarettes and chocolate and tried to talk with them, but unlike all other natives that I have met in the desert, they were withdrawn and hostile and two of them were obviously ill. We managed to communicate to them that I was a doctor and that when our baggage donkeys came up we would have a look in our medical supplies and see if we had something that would help them. They responded by spitting and turning away, and obviously viewed us with suspicion.

The guide had a heated conversation with them in

Arabic, and then speaking to me in French said that this group of eight men had come from Niger to Algeria looking for work, had been turned away as they had no work permits or entry permits, so were now walking over the plateau to try and find work in Chad, but again he said there was no chance of there being any as they had no papers or work permits for Chad and they would be sent on again.

These men were ill, thin and starved, with no possessions of any value, no food with them, just this goatskin of water. I thought perhaps I might be able to do something for the sick ones, but once they'd filled their goatskin with water, they shrugged their shoulders and set off on the long journey across the plateau to Chad.

Our guide's protests could not stop them; they shrugged their shoulders and went.

That night we camped in some caves in an area called Timsumatec, and after dinner sat huddled round a wood fire, smoking and talking, with our donkey boys and guides just round the corner with their own fire. A cold wind was blowing and we all had on every piece of spare clothing. As we were about to settle down after some singing and the passing round of whisky, I saw a light flashing in the distance about a mile away. Now the plateau is so remote that you just don't see lights at this time of night and the donkey boys were already asleep round the glowing embers of their fire, so I set off to investigate. My immediate thoughts were that these starving desperate men had come to slit our throats in the night. I explored as far as I could without seeing anything and thankfully came back to the camp, very relieved not to have found anybody. We had three women with us and I was concerned about their safety.

The light appeared once more, about half an hour later, now closer, and I set off again, worried about what I was going to find. I was pleased that this time a member of our party followed me out. I didn't feel quite so alone, and I gave much credit to him because physical violence was not in his make-up, but he wasn't going to see me going out into the darkness on my own. I tried to trace the light source, but it kept going and coming, then suddenly out of the darkness loomed a great shape which I was about to hit when a voice said, '*Je cherche les ans.*' It was one of the donkey drivers, all dressed up in his best, supposedly looking for the donkeys. He disappeared after some conversation and I made sure that the women of our party slept together and that we were close at hand. I thought that our female tourists were much more likely to be the object of the search than the donkeys.

So it wasn't my eight men from Niger.

As I lay in the warmth of my sleeping bag that night I thought of those eight men with no food and little clothing, who had set out from their tribe to earn money in Djanet, with no knowledge of the complexities of modern life, and no understanding that you can't enter countries without passports or work without a permit. There they were, trekking across the plateau in mid-winter with no protection, on a journey to absolute hopelessness. There was no chance of them not being turned back once they got to the other side of the plateau and when they had retraced their steps, they would be thrown out again. It seemed they would be damned eternally to walking to and fro.

This haunted me because these men were tribesmen. Tuaregs, men of fine breeding and stature, destroyed by our modern society, not able to communicate or accept the advice that what they were doing was leading them nowhere.

They would have left their tribes with such hopes of bringing back money for their families, and already they had probably been travelling for some months. Civilisation had spoilt their simple pastoral way of life and not equipped them to cope with life in the modern world.

Ever since that night, whenever I read of primitive people starting to be educated, and claims of the civilisation of remote areas, I think first of the proud Tuareg in his tent with his flocks of sheep and goats, and then I think of the eight endlessly walking men from Niger – and I wonder, why can't we just leave things alone?

20. Thirty Years Gone

Six of us were sitting in the biology lab at Epsom College in December 1944. We were a sub-section of the medical six who had been sitting the first MB and the Conjoint Board Pre-Medical Examination. These were our last few days as schoolboys. The war was pressing on to its bloody conclusion; we were too young and isolated to appreciate its horrors, and indulged in schoolboy fugues of heroism and daring acts. None of us wanted to go straight to medical school. We had opted as one man for the Fleet Air Arm where, with pride, we'd learnt that the average life of a pilot in the air was thirty-six hours. What would they think at the youth club when we came in wearing our uniforms?

I discussed the situation with my father, who always kept me on a loose rein. He thought some experience before medical school would be valuable, that the Fleet Air Arm certainly sounded glamorous, but the way things were going, the war would be over shortly, and the chances of reaching air crew would be virtually nil; I would be wasting my time for a few years doing some mundane job. If I really wanted to do something valuable which would widen my experience and make a contribution to society, why not go down the mines for a year? The Bevin Scheme was under way at the time and men were being conscripted for the mines as they were for the armed forces.

The streak in me that loved doing the out-of-the-ordinary had persisted, and the idea fired my imagination. So I went to the Labour Exchange and asked if I could go down the mines for a year. They said they would be delighted to have me; as a medical student I could come out when I liked, and so I signed on there and then. My father's wisdom prevailed and my five friends who went into the Fleet Air Arm spent five months making paths across airfields with clinker and coke and were then given an early discharge. Thus, on 1 February 1945, I came to be setting out for Doncaster with a bright Ministry of Labour label on my case.

Proudly flashing the label as if it were a DSC or at least a captain's pips, I reached Askern Main Colliery, one of the initial training establishments for Bevin Boys in the Yorkshire coalfields.

I was at Askern for a month, a member of a very mixed bunch. I, with my boy scout's enthusiasm, could not understand why my colleagues were not delighted to be able to go down pits and dig out coal. Most of my colleagues were either from industry where, with the reduction in arms production, they had become redundant and had been conscripted for the mines, or were air crew, many of whom had been training in Canada where, again, there was a reduction in personnel with the war drawing to a close. When I look back and think of the adjustment that these officer cadets had to make, one minute being fêted in Canada in a smart uniform

89

and with reasonable pay, then almost overnight being transformed into coal miners, it must have been almost too much to bear.

There were one or two straight conscripts who were neither redundant factory workers nor ex-Air Force. These included a concert pianist, and one poor lad who had never strayed from his father's estates, where he had a private tutor, his only glimpse of the public being when he was supervising hop-picking on the family estate. In one of our many political discussions – and this was at the time of the socialist revolution – poor 'Lord Tom', as he was called, in a very hostile environment put forward the suggestion that the only possible government was that of genuine aristocracy. On reflection, after thirty years, I think he was probably right.

There was a certain apathy about most of my fellow Bevin Boys as in addition to the change of circumstances, there was a marked reduction in the amount of money they had. Many had been making very good money working long hours as workers in Midland factories.

We were good company, though. There were the various dances and social engagements, and one of the local farmers asked a group of us round for ham and eggs in quantities that I had not seen since before the war.

We had our delightful eccentrics: two brothers and a cousin who bore the name of a famous cough medicine had had a row with their fathers and volunteered for the mines that day. They distinguished themselves when being posted to their pit near Nottingham by living at the most fashionable hotel in the town and crossing the lounge in the evening in their pit boots and helmets on their way to their rooms for a wash.

We were housed at Askern in the proverbial army Nissen hut, with stoves, bunk beds and lockers. We ate at the pit canteen for lunch but came back to the hostel for our evening meal. Our day was split up between lectures, physical training and visits down the pit. The lectures were very simple, about life underground, and I still have the books that I won for being top of the examination. Physical training was the routine stuff with a regular ex-Guards sergeant.

Visits underground were quite different. This was a new experience for all of us. Half the colliery was in production and the other half was used for the training of Bevin Boys. I never liked, and know of nobody who likes, going down in a pit cage. You hurtle down into the darkness to the accompaniment of the hissing of compressed air pipes and, usually, dripping water, and with the slowing down of the cage at the bottom feel you are shooting back up to the top again.

Only once have I been in a pit cage when anything unusual happened. On this occasion there was some technical fault. We had neared the bottom and then were lifted back up halfway, quarter of a mile from daylight and quarter of a mile from the bottom. Tension mounted steadily. We were hopeless, helpless, and did not know what was going on. I could feel the tension rising. One cannot contemplate shinning up a quarter-of-a-mile rope, or sliding down one. Happily, after ten minutes, we went down and were got off on to safe ground.

The training shaft at Askern Colliery had the added refinement of a two-tier cage, of which only the top tier was used. The reason for this was apparent on our first trip. We huddled together as the cage plunged down, thinking we were almost certainly descending to our deaths. The end of the journey finished in a loud splash which confirmed our worst fears. What in fact was happening was that the sump (which is the space below where the cage stops to unload in the pit bottom) was full of water into which the bottom tier of the cage used to splash and unload the top tier. It was all too much for our pianist who was claustrophobic and was quite hysterical. He made two or three more attempts to go down the pit, but was eventually discharged as being unfit to serve underground.

We climbed along tunnels and through coal faces, and spent half a day working in a place called Garsides, which was extremely hot. After four weeks in which we had just got to know each other, we were split up and posted to various collieries in the South Yorkshire field. A few of us managed to stick together and were posted to Dinnington Main Colliery, near Sheffield. We had been living in hostels till now, and were transferred to another hostel (Nissen huts, bunk beds again) but were expected to find accommodation in Dinnington village once we had settled in.

During our first month at Dinnington we were put through a hardening-up process, which meant that at six o'clock every morning we had to report at the pit top and unload a twenty-ton railway wagon full of stones or clinkers. This was our day's work. Here we acquired our blisters, developed our shovelling muscles and, as the old miner in charge of us said, 'If you shovel at an elephant's feet, it will fall over.'

Now toughened up, I was ready to work underground. I hated my first job down below. It was working in the pit bottom, assisting in putting tubs on and off the cage. It was cold, noisy and relentless. There seemed to be streams of tubs loaded with coal coming at you all the time. You stopped a tub by pushing what was known as a 'locker' between the spokes of the running wheel, which acted as an instant brake. You had to be careful not to put your hand in or under the wheel, and if you missed with your locker a stream of tubs could come pouring down, smashing the cage and halting the drawing of coal. As far as I remember the drawing rate was sixty times an hour, and one only had a few seconds to unlock a tub, push the empty tubs off the cage with the full tubs, shut the gates and leap back. There were horrific tales told of men catching their sleeves in the up-going cage, and I hated it.

There are two shafts in a coal mine: one the down-going shaft in which the air is drawn into the mine, and the other the up-going, where the stale, but now warm air is drawn out, and I was at the bottom of the down shaft. In mid-winter it was very cold.

I had come to be a coal miner and would settle for nothing less than a pick and shovel. I was only going to be down a year, and I wanted to do the whole lot. Colliers were the fighter pilots of the industry. They were the real men who had a confident swagger, knowing that whatever anybody else did, they were the men that mattered and the rest were just supporting troops. When, eventually, I was a collier myself, I likened the experience of the work very much to that of the small amount of rock climbing that I had done: there is the same physical effort, some hazards, and achievement and accomplishment at the end of the day.

After four weeks on the pit bottom I was moved to a job further in the pit, which was reckoned to be one of the softest jobs going. In a little airless passage we had a compressed-air prop-straightening machine. Nearly all the pit props and roof supports (bars) were iron. The bent, twisted ones were brought off the coal faces to be straightened in this machine.

I was Ben Burgess's assistant. He was an old collier, past retiring age, and a great character who was delighted to have a medical student as his side-kick. The job was tedious to the extreme. It was so hot and airless that it was very difficult to keep awake; the job had no incentive. Sometimes we would run out of props and bars and would sit, fighting to keep awake. The worst sin you can commit underground is to fall asleep. It is a bit like falling asleep in the snow – you may never wake up.

We used to have visits from the deputies (foremen) and the overman (foreman in charge of underground shift), who would all pass the time of day, and the few remaining pit ponies – under-worked, over-fed, savage beasts – used to come with their terrified drivers to carry our props away in small trucks.

My friend Albert, who is now a successful Birmingham jeweller, came flying past one day, hanging on to the bit of his aggressive pony, not being able to stop him for a further half-mile, with always the danger that the pony would pull the tub off the rails and bring down the roof of the narrow underground passages in which they travelled. These were called 'supply gates' and there was just room for a tub to pass. They were only about five feet in height – tall enough for the pony but not the driver, and there was continual subsidence, with gangs called 'rippers' maintaining them and seeing that the average height and width was maintained.

My days with Ben seemed to go on forever. If you have been half-asleep in a boring lecture you know the agony of being nine hours a day in this situation. Ben warned me of the perils of the coal face. I had a safe job with him, but it was the coal face for me – I did want the complete experience. So, after only two months underground, I was offered the job of coal-face borer.

This was by far the worst job for me on the coal face. It hadn't the sheer strenuous exhaustion of actually getting coal, but the frustrations and the difficult positions one had to get into to bore more than made up for this.

In 1945, in the colliery that I worked, the coal face was usually about three hundred yards in length – a four-foot seam, a four-foot sandwich of coal between a rock floor and a rock roof. The depth of Dinnington Colliery is about half a mile, and we were three miles out from the pit bottom, travelling the first two miles by a paddy train (open benches on a small railway) and walking the last mile through small tunnels. The three-hundred-yard front of coal on the preceding shift before the colliers arrived would be undercut by a coal-cutting machine to a depth of six feet, the machine removing the bottom six inches of coal. At each end of the face were roadways along which material required for use at the coal face was brought. Running at right angles from the centre of the coal face was another roadway, the 'loader gate', coal being carried away from the face along this by a large conveyor belt. Smaller belts running from each end of the face emptied the coal that the colliers were getting on to this loader belt.

The stint which was the daily allotment of each collier was a seven-and-a-half-yard length of coal face. This was marked on the roof and the collier had to clear the coal in this area to a depth of six feet. He started by cleaning out the loose dust left by the coal cutter, undermining the coal as much as he could. When he had a clear place under the coal, he would call for the borer, who with a six-foot drill would somehow contort himself and bore a hole on the collier's instruction, which later a deputy (foreman) would come and fire an explosive charge in, hopefully blowing to the back of the cut so the collier could then start shifting the coal on to the face conveyor belt. The collier's work was finished only when all his coal was cleared and he had to put up supporting props and timbers in the empty space.

There was a three-shift system in which the colliers would remove the coal to a depth of six feet, then men who were known as panners and packers would move the face conveyor belts forward six feet and extend the loader belt six feet and withdraw the timber that had been previously supporting the roof before the conveyor belt was moved. Stone-wall packs were put up in the waste behind where the coal had been extracted before the props were withdrawn to help break up the roof's surface as it descended.

In 1945 face drills were driven by compressed air and there was a compressed-air pipe the whole length of the face. This was covered with lumps of loose coal and coal dust, and had coupling valves every fifteen to twenty yards. The face borer had first to blow out any dust from the pipes without getting his head blown off, then with a six-foot drill and thirty yards of rubber tubing, had to scramble up and down the coal face as the colliers requested holes for blowing their coal. He had to find the valves hidden in the dust, make sure his machine did not jam, and check that he had sharp bits for his drills. We only had hand lamps, which had to be carried. It was the nearest to Dante's Inferno that I have been – there was the noise of falling coal, the shouts and screams of the colliers who wanted 'the bloody borer', dust, acrid smoke following the face as shots were fired further along it. And if the shot had not been placed deeply enough (a flanker), the whole face, which was part of the air system, became thick with blinding smoke.

On some faces the conveyor belt was put right up to the coal face and the collier had to dig a hole in for himself to get working, whereas the poor borer had to travel up and down the three-hundred-yard length, hopping in and out of the waste behind the coal face that might come down at any minute, clamber over the conveyor belt with huge lumps of coal trying to knock him off all the time, and perch sometimes across the belt with coal whizzing past between his legs as he fought to drill a six-foot hole into the coal. His other duties were to put props, clay for shot firing, and wooden nogs (which were used to stop props slipping) on the end of the face belts so the colliers could pull supplies off for themselves as the material passed them. It was an absolute nightmare. You were nobody's friend.

Most of the seams at Dinnington were between four foot and four foot six inches high, which was ideal for shovelling in the coal face but meant that the borer was operating in a height of under three feet, with a sagging roof beyond the belt and the elevated belt with coal pouring down it.

On my first day as a borer I was sent to Five's Face, where the coal was thicker than anywhere else in the pit, about five feet from roof to floor, and getting about was rather easier. Halfway through my first shift I saw everyone down tools and get off the face very quickly. I thought, 'Ah! Snap (lunch) time,' and wandered slowly off the face, surprised at the noise of the creaking and grinding of the roof, and even more surprised when the coal face behind me started to burst, shooting lumps of coal right across the belt. Only when I got off the face and somebody grabbed me, not too politely, did I realise there was what was known as a dreaded 'top weight' on where, with a major rock subsidence, a coal face, in spite of props and timbers, can be squashed flat in a matter of minutes. This was the only top weight I experienced in over two years underground, and I was too naive to know its implications.

My days were long. I used to get up at four o'clock and catch the 4.15 bus to the pit. We used to huddle in a telephone booth, six of us, waiting for the bus to come. Then to the pit baths, undress and put our clothes in a clean locker, walk across to the other side of the baths and get into our dirty pit clothes, fill our water bottles, then go down to the pit just after five. I found I could rarely eat on the coal face. The only thing that I could ever get down were odd slices of bread and dripping. Anything else gave me indigestion. I had a five-pint water tin we called a 'Dudley'. I could always have managed with ten pints.

I would be out of the pit, if all went well, by about 2.30, then shower and wash, change, and eat lunch in the pit-head canteen – my first meal of the day. For the first few months I used to go to bed when I got home and have a couple of hours from 3.30 to 5.30, but waking at 5.30 was like waking from the dead and I felt like a ghost for the rest of the evening. Eventually I dropped the afternoon nap and decided that five hours' sleep a night was enough, and used to go to bed around 10.30 to 11.00, getting up at 4 a.m.

In my afternoon-sleeping days, waking up exhausted and stiff after my two hours, I discovered a most sensual experience: putting on the clean, starched shirts that my landlady, 'Auntie Bradley', had laundered for me. It was one of the few erotic experiences for which I could summon sufficient energy.

Social life was very limited. Sheffield was man-hours away by bus, and most of the time I was too tired.

In my second year I did go to Rotherham to night school to do some organic chemistry, but in my first year the highlight of the week was a trip to Sheffield on a Saturday evening. It was still a six-day week then, and one could not get away from the pit before about two. Even as a coal-face borer my wages were only about £3 a week, and by the time I paid for my lodgings and my lunches at the pit canteen I just had enough money to get me to Sheffield by bus to the City Hall for a dance. I used to have an orangeade in the first interval and a trifle in the second interval, and when I saw the City Hall in all its splendour with the revolving globe of reflected light, I thought I had made it big. If only the chaps at school could see me now!

The mining community took to us. I do not remember a single occasion when anybody was deliberately unkind. They were patient, hard-working and very good-natured.

There were about forty thousand Bevin Boys in the coal-mining industry at this time. Most had settled in pretty well, and the underground haulage systems were very often dependent on their man-power. This was certainly the case at Dinnington. Few took regular jobs at the coal face, but one of the exceptions was a delightful lad called Dennis Abbot who had made the transition from air crew in Canada to coal-face worker most successfully. He was on the opposite shift to me so I did not see a great deal of him.

The coal face had a camaraderie and humour of its own. The safety of each man was dependent on how carefully all his neighbours set their pit-props, and there was a high standard of care and workmanship. The humour was rough but nonetheless witty and I, who had come straight from a public school, was very glad of the paternalism they showed me.

I was a coal-face borer for three months, itching to have a go with a pick and shovel. I would be paid more, and there was always something degrading about being a borer – you were at people's beck and call, and the whole face could be at a standstill if you did not get your pipes blown out.

At last the great day came.

'No borers needed on Five's. You can have a go at a stint, Bob lad,' said the deputy. Pleased as Punch, I swaggered off with my pick and heart-shaped shovel. I was really going to be a collier at last.

My first stint was on Three's face, which had a certain notoriety. It had bad roof faults, which made timbering and propping difficult, and had slips where the coal cut narrowed out and rock and coal had to be taken together. It was also the furthest out, where one not only had to walk a mile and a half uphill along a narrow, low supply road to the face, but also, owing to the ventilation system down below, where the further out the face was, the hotter it became.

We used to walk to the face in our pit clothes – trousers, jacket and, for some reason, waistcoats were always fashionable underground. But working gear comprised solely of a pair of short cotton pants, heavy pit safety boots with metal toecaps, and fibre pit helmets. Although head lamps with the battery attached to the waist were becoming the fashion, at that time we had only rather heavy electric lamps in the shape of miniature lighthouses with one man in six carrying in addition an oil lamp for gas testing.

Working at the coal face on a stint was by far the hardest work I have ever experienced. On this particular face each man had a stint of seven and a half yards of coal face, the thickness of the coal being three foot six inches to four foot six inches. This had to be cleared to a depth of six feet. It had been previously undercut and usually had what is known as a 'breaking-in' hole blown. That is, at the end of each stint before the colliers arrive, on the previous shift a hole had been bored in the coal and an explosive charge fired so that he could break into his face of coal, reach the back of the cut, and then work down the length of his coal.

Theoretically, with the coal undercut and a gap between it and the rock floor, the fired shot should have broken through to the back of the cut, making coal-getting easy. But too often it was fired without the loose coal from the cut being cleared, and it jammed solid making it almost as bad as having to hack through solid coal. Once you had broken right through to the back of the cut, the coal came away easily and you could follow it down the face, timbering as you went.

We arrived at the coal face at six o'clock and I eventually cleared my stint with the help of a collier on the next stint by two o'clock. There is no stop for lunch-time breaks – just an occasional swig at the water bottle, the terrible race of flying shovels heaving lumps and the back-breaking work of putting up metal bars with metal props which, if not put in properly, could fly out like catapults and maim you.

I was completely exhausted after my first shift. And this became my daily task. For sheer physical graft and endeavour I have never known its equal. It was hot, noisy, dusty, with smoke coming from shots being fired;

the work was always just a bit more than I could manage.

I was on a stint continually from June 1945 till December 1946. It was exhausting – completely exhausting – work, but had a particular satisfaction of its own that I have never met elsewhere; for once you were finished, you were finished; the next day brought a fresh battle but each day brought a fresh achievement, and you left the battlefield and then went to a world outside.

In much of my life since, particularly in medicine, there are overhanging worries and fears continuing and overlapping all the time, but as a coal-face worker, apart from the overall worry that one might have about mining, you went in, did your stint, and came off. There was a measure to your work of finishing which has never applied to the rest of my working life, and you could not in any way, apart from personal physical fitness, start on the next day's work.

I remember VE Day in Rotherham and walking home from Rotherham to Dinnington on a moonlit night. I remember the coming of the five-day week, and this made a real change to my life. The joy of finishing on a Friday afternoon and knowing I was a free agent until Monday morning! I was fortunate that I had some relatives in Maltby and Rotherham and I could visit them at weekends; and once the five-day week started, in the winter months I played rugby for Sheffield at Abbeydale Park. This gave a new contrast to my work as I had become immersed in the mining community. Joining the rugby club (and Abbeydale Park had an extremely well equipped, gracious clubhouse) I was back into the world I had come from.

Sometime in 1945 I had a letter from the Ministry of Labour giving me a number, inferring that I would be doing a full stint of National Service. I made no protest about our original agreement. It seemed only fair; and anticipating a discharge towards the end of 1947, I applied for admission to St Mary's Hospital, London.

I had attended a few union meetings and was a member of the National Union of Mineworkers, but was never too involved. I went down to London for an interview at St Mary's. I was the only professional collier they had considered and, to my surprise, not long after I was back, I received a letter from the dean saying that they were creating a number of places for ex-servicemen in January that year; they had applied to the Ministry of Labour for my release, but had been turned down.

At the last National Union of Mineworkers meeting I had been to, knowing that I was applying for a hospital place, they said, 'Don't worry, Bob lad; as soon as they offer you a place in the hospital, we'll see you get your release.' I took my dean's letter to the NUM and on 20 December 1946, I received a letter from the Ministry of Labour saying that I could go to St Mary's after all, and a letter from St Mary's confirming that there was a place for me.

I did my last shift, and forty-eight hours later started at Mary's as a medical student. But this was not to be the end of mining for me. Somehow it was in my blood. There were times when I thought of going back for a further year as, at that time, coal-mining was much more important economically than a medical student missing a year of study. But this was really an excuse I think to get out of the rather tedious bookwork that I found myself involved with. I had to take my first MB examination again, and in the long vacation of the summer of 1947, the Coal Board fixed me up with a pit in the Nottingham-Rufford Colliery, near Mansfield. I stayed in a theatrical boarding house. I was on the haulage for a week to acclimatise myself to underground conditions and then spent the next six weeks working on the coal face. I was teamed up with a collier in the corner of the face where the coal was some distance from the coal belt and had to be thrown in two moves – the collier to me, and then me to the coal belt. I soon rediscovered a few muscles that I had forgotten, not to mention a few blisters.

I had thought, with my interest in mining, that I might do industrial medicine, and in 1949 I again went back to the pits in the long summer vacation, this time to Bolsover Colliery in Derbyshire. Here, when I arrived, the pit was on holiday for a week and I spent this week working with some rippers, i.e. men who maintain the roadways in the pits by continually enlarging and propping, channelling out the roadway as the roof slowly and remorselessly descends.

It was at Rufford that I had a week in an eighteen-inch seam where they were heading out a new face. This was the only time that I worked in such low conditions, and it was so low here that you either shovelled on your stomach or came off from the face and returned on your back. There was no room for your pelvis between the roof and the floor.

Both at Rufford and Bolsover the miners spoilt me and used to take me off drinking in Nottingham at night. At Bolsover I lodged with a miner and his family. There was no connecting bus, so this meant a three-mile walk to the pit, and back, each day.

Pay and conditions between 1946, 1947 and 1949 improved considerably. In my time at Dinnington as a coal-face borer my pay was around £3 12s per week and, even as an almost full-blown collier on the face, £5 10s was my maximum pay packet. However, both at Rufford and Bolsover, although spending part of the time on the haulage and never being on the full collier's rate when at the face, my average pay for the six and seven week periods was over £14 a week.

Industrial medicine was not for me however. I could not reconcile my medical training to routine medical examinations and the checking of equipment at the pit-head ambulance rooms. In 1961, while attending the Writers' Summer School at Swanwick, Derbyshire, I did go down the local colliery and visited a two-foot seam where they had a mechanical coal-getter working, but being fat, forty and unfit, just crawling along the face exhausted me.

Some years ago I had a funeral to attend near Dinnington so slipped back and spent a couple of hours there. My old landlady and her husband (Auntie and Ike Bradley) had not changed a bit. It was as if time had stood still. They still had a budgerigar, but Ike was no longer down the pit. I had last seen them twenty years before, when I went up for a visit.

I phoned one man, Albert Platts, who had been a deputy (foreman) when I was doing my Bevin Boy stint, and I had changed in the intervening time from being a 9 stone 10 pound stripling to a bald, stout, forty-nine-year-old. Albert hardly seemed to have changed at all. I had pulled him out of his bath on a cold winter's afternoon. 'Do you remember me, Albert?' I said. Albert looked puzzled. 'Do you come from Huddersfield? No, by Christ, I remember you,' said Albert, pulling up his trouser leg and showing me a scar that I had forgotten. Oblivious to the world, on my stint one day, swinging my pick, I did not hear Albert come up behind me to see if I needed any shots fired, and had swung the sharp, light-weight pick we used into his leg. He said it was his language that day that had completed my education.

It was difficult seeing the pit now surrounded by the colliers' cars and rows of new houses to realise that I used to work there and was so much part of the local scene. I saw the miners trooping across from the pithead baths to the pit. I could see the winding cage wheel spinning on top of its box-like tower thirty years ago.

When I look back on my experience, and as a doctor I have had a fairly wide experience of life (I have done some travelling and visited most of the Western European countries, as well as a couple of trips to the Sahara) I would say that British (and particularly the Yorkshire) coal-miners are the nearest to what we can call being typically British, and more so than any other group I have met. They are durable, obstinate, loyal, warm-hearted, kind, generous and industrious, both in their work and play. They survived the periods of economic hardship between the two wars by sticking together, and have never ceased to stick together. This, to some extent, makes them vulnerable, because it allows them to be manipulated. They will come running when anyone shouts a rallying call and can be in a situation not of their choosing by their sheer loyalty. But they are quick to learn and nobody, choose who they are, will manipulate them for long.

Fables

21. The Queen's Champion

The Queen, who was the fairest in all the land and who was said by the wise men to be the fairest of all queens, had come to take part in the time-honoured tradition of choosing her Champion.

The custom was that when the Queen was in the full bloom of her womanhood, all the men of the nation who had some particular skill or prowess would come to the four-day games and compete before her.

Having seen the best men giving of their best, the Queen had then to choose her Champion, giving two reasons to the populace – those of character and prowess – as to why her choice stood above the rest.

From then on, the chosen man was to be known as the Queen's Champion. He would be closer to the Queen than any other man and have almost the rights of a king.

It was not only physical prowess that counted. Poets, minstrels, orators, even politicians could come and show their hand. So the great men of the nation congregated. The runners and horsemen from the plains, the javelin throwers and wrestlers from the mountains, and the men of culture from the seats of learning. Many of these were indeed mighty men and their performances drew roars of appreciation from the crowds. There were so many men with great skills that no man stood out as a popular choice.

Amongst the competitors was a youth. Most competitors had entered for one event only, showing their maximum skill at one pursuit. But the youth had entered every event and as one competition ended, he had to go on to the next one. Even orating.

The youth came last in some events, but he did better in others. His best performance was in stone throwing where he came in fourth, just missing a prize, as prizes were only given to the first three. But none of this seemed to bother him and he entered each and every event with vigour.

The final event ended and the crowd waited expectantly as the Queen, in all her beauty, walked to the dais.

The competitors stood in the group of their own particular event. The youth who had been in every event and did not belong to any group had to stand on his own, alone and to one side.

The Queen spoke. 'My people,' she said, 'it gladdens my heart to know that we have a nation of men of such ability and prowess. Many men are fit, on the showing of these games, to be my Champion but I can only choose one. And I choose the youth who stands alone.'

A great murmur ran through the crowd at the Queen's choice. How could she possibly justify it, having seen the great stature of some of the competitors?

When the noise settled she went on.

'For his character,' she said. 'Most of you entered only one event but the youth entered every one. Some he fared badly at, some he did better at, and in one event he nearly won a prize. In every event he entered, he did enough to be called a legitimate participant of the particular craft. But above all, he was the only one of you who was unashamed to show his deficiencies before his queen.'

'For his prowess,' she said. 'Whilst you rested between events, as he was engaged in every event he had no time to rest, he showed more energy than any of you. If it were my wish that a mountain should be removed from my kingdom, he is the only one of you I could call on, as he would tackle it baldheaded. And with his energy he might even one day move a mountain.'

'This is my chosen Champion. Robe him and prepare him for me.'

There was a great roar of approval from the populace.

The Queen's senior handmaiden fell at her feet.

'Your Majesty,' she said, 'never in the history of our nation has a queen chosen her Champion with such wisdom. This is indeed an historic day.'

'Wisdom? Nuts,' said the Queen. 'That crafty lout crept into my bed chamber last night. I didn't choose him. He chose me. I have hardly been able to keep my eyes off him.

'And that prowess . . . Phew!'

22. The Bridge

She sat watching him, busy at work on the other side of the water.

She said, 'I do admire the energy and aggression in the way you work. How can you spend so much time building a bridge when you are running a successful farm?'

He said, 'It is just a question of motivation, and that is a very long story.'

She said, 'How long will it take to build, to reach my side, so that I can cross over safely when I wish?'

He said, 'Well, this is a very special sort of a bridge. I can only build half of it as far as the middle of the water. If you want a whole bridge, you will have to build the other half on your own from your side. It will have to be the same size and strength as the bridge on my side.'

She said, 'Can't I just lean a plank across when you have finished your half? I'm not really a builder at all.'

He said, 'No. Each half must be as big and as strong as the other. You will have to work just as hard as I have

112

done. If we don't, we might fall through the middle.'

She said, 'This is awful. You know I can't possibly work as hard as you. It would ruin my hands. I am not strong enough and I haven't the time. You know I want to be the world's best pastry cook. Most of my time is spent thinking up new recipes. I am beginning to worry, and that's awful. I thought at last I had found something stable and secure, something that would always be there, something I would have for ever.'

He continued to build.

She cried, 'You are building that bloody bridge so fast that you are either going to blow up or make it fall in the water, then all your work will be wasted.

'In a short time I have changed from being terribly happy to having one great worry about the speed your side of the bridge is growing. You are different from other men. If they were building a bridge they would do it in a day, with helicopters and bulldozers. They jump out of cars and open doors for us. I've so much to do. I haven't washed up, the beds are unmade, I was going climbing with friends, and I can't get a thing done, wondering whether I should be trying to keep up with you on the bridge.

'And you! You are smiling as if everything is all right, and for God's sake, why have you got that rope around your shoulders?'

He said, smiling, 'Everything is just as it was in the beginning. I am still your very best friend, etc., and always will be. You must try and accept that I am a compulsive bridge builder. If I can't build across, I can build up. Theoretically a strong bridge is proof against fire, flood and earthquake. But bridges are rigid structures and have a vulnerability of their own.

'The only significant thing about me is the rope.

Although the coil is round my shoulders, what you cannot see is that the end of the rope is in my strong right hand.

'Whenever you want to cross the water, all you have to do is shout and I will throw you the rope and pull you over. The rope can also be used if you slip or fall whilst climbing or on a slope. For if you reach for it, you will find you will always be able to pull yourself up. The only thing that is required of you is never to go so far away that I can't reach you with the rope.

'If, in any one of a hundred ways, my bridge building upsets you, providing you let me know, I can always stop and we will always have the rope.'

She said, 'Thank you, I am happy again now; for a time I was worried.'

He said, 'From now on you will have no worry that you have to bear alone.'

He dived into the water and swam to her.

Now, you couldn't hear what they were saying.

Before, they had been shouting because of the distance.

23. The Princess and the Herdsman

The herdsman was shepherding his cattle across the great plain. It was cold and wet, with driving rain. He had been unwell, with ague, for some time. He was listless, easily exhausted, and had difficulty in swallowing his food. He found his work a great burden and lacked motivation and energy.

He decided to camp early for the night, near a ruined castle which, until recently, had been part of a great kingdom. He settled the herd down, and not until then did he begin to make some comfort for himself.

At last he managed to light a fire in the shelter of some rocks, away from the wind and rain. As he sat there looking into the darkness he saw a beautiful woman walking towards him. As she got nearer he could see that she was, without a doubt, a princess of one of the greatest and noblest orders. She was quite beautiful, but had a haunted look about her and her eyes showed shadows of pain and suffering.

She came straight up to him and asked, 'May I join you and seek your protection? There is someone bothering me. I would be most grateful if I could stay with you for a while.'

'By all means,' said the herdsman. 'Come and sit by the fire. But, tell me, why do you look so sad?'

'Recently,' replied the princess, 'I lost my kingdom. I am bereft without it. I just don't know in which direction to go. I am lost and confused. My kingdom was the most beautiful and complete kingdom there ever was.'

They sat talking till late in the night. The herdsman, always one for a pretty face, tried to kiss her cheek, but she backed away and said, 'Please don't do that.'

In the morning the herdsman's ague was worse and he had to move on before he was able to say goodbye properly to his princess.

One week later his travels brought him back near the ruined castle and he made camp. Once more the princess joined him by his fire.

They talked and, for the first time, she came and laid her head on his shoulder and he gently caressed her face and hair with his fingers. As well as talking they cooked and shared some food together.

This became the pattern of their ways.

They would meet regularly at the camp site near the ruined castle. To get to her more often the herdsman had to redouble his efforts with his herd, as he always took great care of it, and he rushed round his tasks with good heart as he knew he would soon see his princess again. He felt more alive and the ague that had been troubling him for some months began to go, and his eating became easier.

At each new meeting around the camp fire their physical intimacies grew. A touch became a caress, a caress would develop into holding and embracing each other, and their lips, which touched only gently at first, became full-blooded kisses with their two mouths minutely exploring each other's.

The princess did not like to be seen with the herdsman. She would hide if anyone approached. She felt guilty about being with him and did not want them to be a subject matter to be talked about.

They not only explored each other's bodies, but also explored each other's minds, and what was good was that the sad princess began to smile and laugh again and the herdsman lost his ague and became well and alive again as tiredness and sickness of the body are often allied to tiredness and sickness of the mind.

The two – the princess and the herdsman – lay by the fire together. The herdsman was almost in a state of bliss. The touch of the princess was like no other, and it was almost enough for him to caress her cool neck with his cheek or draw his forearm gently across her face and lips. They lay like lovers, bodies entwined, with mouths fighting to enter each other's and the herdsman trying to dissolve away the garments that separated them so that their naked bodies could be locked in fulfilment. But when he attempted to slide his hand in her clothes and caress her nakedness she would push him gently away and would look pained and distressed, and the anguish of some deeper inner conflict would be apparent. So they would roll back to their twining and caressing, with the herdsman almost incontinent with physical love and passion, his frustration leaving him exhausted when they parted. At the same time the sadness of the face of the princess increased. It was as if, after every embrace, she had to go off and pay some terrible price for having dared to enjoy the physical contact.

Apart they were gentle with each other, and explained to each other all the duties and commitments that went with the different worlds they came from. She told him of the perfection of the kingdom she had lost, and he of the hard work and commitments of a herdsman.

In their embracing (and it was embracing, never quite love making) they were different. The herdsman lost, intoxicated by the perfect white softness of her body and her touch; the princess detached, half in a dream, recoiling at intimacies but fully involved in the gentle twining, caressing and kissing they had together.

The herdsman could not understand it. He was overcome in a swoon of gentle physical desire and could only seek unthinking fulfilment, whilst the princess suffered as if knowing the further she went, the greater the terrible price she would have to pay. It was almost an impasse.

It was only after their last being together that the herdsman realised what it was that was keeping them apart. He knew the princess had a great and lasting regard for him, and by this time, they had built a great and lasting regard for each other, but when she reached for him physically it was not him she was reaching for but her lost kingdom. That he was warm and kind and responsive was part of the pain she had to bear and each intertwining dream had to finish, and each finish was a realistic waking-up to the fact that the shape she had been caressing was only an imitation of the kingdom she had lost.

Soon after this she came to tell him that she was going to be taken care of by friends for a time. They lived some great distance away.

'What have we? What are we? Tell me before I go,' she said.

'Well,' he replied, 'I am a herdsman and, if you look, you will see how large a herd I have to take care of.'

She looked and was amazed. She had not looked before. 'Why,' she said, 'your herd spreads as far as the eye can see. Do you have to look after them all alone?'

'In a way, yes,' he said. 'The difficulty is that the herd grows all the time and I get tired and exhausted. If you look closely you will see that many of them are sick. I am good with the sick and because of that I attract them, and the sick take more time and energy in being looked after. You see,' he said, 'I am a looker-after of people and animals – a sort of professional comforter.'

'But what of me?' she asked.

'You, my love, my beautiful princess,' he replied, 'are a person apart. As well as having great beauty, you have great talents, many as yet unexplored. It is not in you to play second fiddle, and I see that I have caused you as much distress as I have caused you happiness. You,' he said, 'will never settle for less than a kingdom and although nothing will ever match the size and magnificence of your lost kingdom, there will in time be other kingdoms and, however small in relation to your last one, they will always grow if you are prepared to put more into them than you take out of them. I know these things because I am much older than I look and am wise in the ways of people.'

They had their meal together before she went away, without touching or embracing.

'What about us?' she asked.

'We,' he said, 'are the beginning of a long-lasting and supporting friendship. Even in the sort time we have had, we are both enriched. I am alive and active and well again, thanks to you, and you I have made smile and laugh again, forms of expression I thought you had lost.'

'What will happen to us?' she asked.

He replied, 'I am always about somewhere. There will be no difficulty. I am fortunate in that I can sometimes project myself to places other than the one I am in, and it could be that there will be some times when it is as if you could touch or even smell me in the room with you, and although I am not there, I am really there giving comfort and support.'

She smiled, sadly, and he briefly caressed her cheek with the back of his hand.

'What must I do?' she asked fearfully.

'Your task,' he replied, 'is simple. You must never ever go so far away that I cannot reach you.'

She got up, collected her things, ready to start her journey. As she rose he bent forward to kiss her cheek. She pulled back sharply. 'I don't kiss in public.'

They shook hands and, as she turned to leave, she suddenly turned round as if remembering. 'By the way,' she said, 'you said you were terribly old. You don't look older than fifty. How old are you?'

'You are over nine hundred years out,' he replied. 'I had my thousandth birthday last Tuesday.'

Short Stories

24. Communications

I first saw the girl when I was registering at the hotel. Picking up my key, our eyes met in the mirror behind the clerk's head. She smiled, and something that I can't describe or explain happened to me.

It was three months before my marriage; I had taken Alison, my fiancée, to an industrial conference at a hotel near Dover; not because it had any particular interest but for both of us to escape the ever-mounting fuss of the pre-wedding preparations, which seemed to be everyone's concern except our own.

The girl was accompanied, too – and as I turned from the desk I could see she had a ring on her engagement finger. At the reception I saw her again, sitting near the bar, smiling. She had some unidentifiable gaiety. As I passed near to buy some drinks she beckoned me over.

'Tell me,' she said, 'do you sleep with your secretary?'

'No,' I said, 'and anyway she couldn't come.'

She laughed, and I moved on and bought my drinks.

Alison had a headache after dinner. The weight of

most of the wedding fuss had fallen on her, and she went to bed early, leaving me sitting smoking in the lounge.

Competitors in the mass cross-Channel swim from Calais to Dover were expected in the early hours, and I toyed with the idea of missing some sleep to go and see them arrive. I was sitting in an alcove behind the main door to the dining room, idly watching people pass, when the girl came out. She left the party she was with and came to the table near me, sorting out a magazine from a pile of journals. She hadn't seen me.

'Tell me,' I said, 'do you sleep with yours?'

She turned, startled, smiled and said, 'No – anyway he's gay.'

She stood for a minute looking at me.

'What a pity you're with friends,' she said.

'Vice versa,' I said.

There was a pause.

'If your friends aren't channel swimmers,' I said, 'we could go and cheer the winner home.'

'Fine,' she said, 'meet me here at three.' Then she turned and hurried to catch up with her friends at the far end of the lounge.

I went up to my room, passing Alison's door with her neat, plain, expensive shoes outside, and lay on my bed wondering. I smoked and tried to read. I wasn't impatient or restless, and for once time ticked evenly by. Sometimes minutes get muddled up with hours, and hours which you think you have stored safely in reserve disappear like minutes; but this night the hours moved properly on in quarters.

At two o'clock I washed and shaved, willing the noise of my electric razor to be quiet, and at quarter to three went down to the deserted lounge to find her sitting in the half-dark waiting for me. We let ourselves out of the rear entrance of the hotel into the car park, got into my car and drove off to the coast and parked in a field on top of the main headland. I turned the headlamps off, sat back in the corner of the driving seat, then turned my head towards her.

'Tell me,' she said, 'did you ever hear the story of . . . ?'

And this became our language.

From the beginning there was no need for physical contact, no soft touch or endearing word. It was sufficient to sit back in opposite corners of the front seat and tell outrageous stories, to laugh and look. I never even knew who won the race.

The only stories that I can remember were about an old colonel on leave from India and his prowess with a prostitute he picked up, and a complicated tale about the size of a man's masculine endowment being related to his shoe size. (It involved a lady who, having been entertained by the coalman who wore size fourteen boots, not only thanked him for his services but also pressed money on him to buy new boots as his present pair must have been pinching him.)

Of all the stories we told these two were the best and became our password.

I couldn't see her in the glow from the dashboard, but as the hours passed, daylight came creeping into the car, gently lighting up her face.

We met every morning at three for five mornings, returning to the hotel at about 6.30 a.m. We kept this compartment of time to ourselves and never met or acknowledged each other during the day. I never felt tired and was able to give Alison some part of my new energy and build her up for the great day just twelve weeks off.

I gave the best speech that I've given at any conference, and words that before I could never command came flowing to me. It was only when at last I got back to the quiet of my room I could lie waiting for the feast of our excursions.

I knew that earlier each night her fiancé, if he were her fiancé, used to fumble his way into her room, hoping that this would be *the* night, but I knew equally well that whatever prospects the future held, there would be no arrival in the promised land for him this week.

We were at peace, sitting apart, laughing, studying each other's faces, and telling our terrible stories.

On our last morning we left our spot on the Downs early and spent the last half-hour having coffee in an all-night transport café. We drove back to the hotel, and as she got out I said, 'By the way, I think you're super.'

'Vice versa,' she said, and went off to her room.

I have never tried to contact her or follow her, in fact, I never knew her name.

Twelve weeks later I married Alison, and life has since been full with children, business, school fees, golf, Rotary, garden and the other thousand small worries of the day.

But I have never forgotten that girl and one small part of my eye is always looking for her.

I know that someday, sometime, somewhere, we'll meet again.

I know that she'll smile and say, 'Hi, Colonel!'

And I'll say, 'God, my boots are pinching.'

And in some strange, beautiful way this will be enough.

25. The Man in the White Cotton Gloves

Nobody saw him without them – he always wore white cotton gloves.

He came to our town the day after the vicar was taken to London for a brain operation. He arrived unexpectedly and unannounced at the Church House in a pair of shabby flannels, a well-worn coat with leather elbows, a battered, much-travelled suitcase, and the thing that was a puzzle us so – his white cotton gloves.

I am the chemist in our small market town, and soon after his arrival he came to me for some ointment balm. I concluded that he had eczema on both hands and, judging from what Mrs Brown – the housekeeper at Church House – reported, he must have had it on his feet as well; it appeared that he always washed his own gloves and socks, and sometimes she found blood on his sheets in the morning.

Owing to the vicar's illness over the past few months, things had begun to slide in the town; pettiness, meanness, scandal and whisperings had started to grow. The church congregation, which had been kept going by the curate from the next parish, had started to fall away, and the circle of spitefulness and malcontent grew, and became a circle of viciousness. It seemed that the worst in all of us was beginning to come out.

I am not a churchman, and at that time things were at their lowest for me as well. I felt I had been robbed when buying the chemist's business: money was owing and creditors were closing in. My wife and I, after ten years of sordid bickering, had called it a day, and she had gone off to her mother's with the three children.

I was a mean man in a mean town and I repeated each bit of gossip and evil over the counter with relish, hoping to drag others down with me.

Before we realised it, the man in the white cotton gloves had settled down among us. He seemed to start his day quietly, and moved through the town gently and unobtrusively, visiting from house to house. He did not discriminate between church and chapel, godly and ungodly, and when I looked back afterwards I realised it didn't seem strange that he had entry to all these houses. He came, as he came into mine, as though he were expected.

In four weeks, somehow the meanness left the town. I don't know why, but people were no longer spiteful, and the church was full. I never heard any of his sermons, but I was told that he spoke them quietly and gently – telling simple stories, with simple homilies. They didn't appear to give any profound message but they all left a mark.

He was always shabby, but at the end of that month no one could be quite sure what he did wear.

Wednesday the twenty-third was my day. I was still trying to be spiteful and hurt people, but I couldn't get anyone to join me. I sat alone that night in my empty

house, and for the first time I looked at the emptiness of
my life. I had failed in business; I had failed my family;
I had failed myself. I had a shop full of remedies that
could take me out of this world, and it seemed the only
way out of my bitterness and loneliness. I hated everything; I loathed myself. Death would be a blessed relief.
I went into my dispensary to make up my final potion.

As I came round the corner of the counter, I was
startled to find 'him' standing in the shop. We walked
through to the living room and started to talk together
quietly and I do not recall all he said. This I do
remember – I was anti-Christian and I taxed him with
the Crucifixion and the meaning of the Cross. His reply
surprised me – he said he had always considered that
Christ was a very lucky mortal man to have the
opportunity to die as he did, and in such circumstances.
He said that so many other men through the centuries
had died for much smaller things with just as much
bravery and fortitude, and with less to hope for.

We talked the night through; he left as dawn was
breaking, and as I showed him out of the door I noticed
the tiredness of his face, his threadbare clothes and the
poverty of his white cotton gloves.

I saw him only once more after that.

That day I started with a new heart, and a new face,
and I don't remember looking back since. By 7.30 a.m.
I had cleaned the house and dusted the shop, and I had
more strength and vigour than I had had for a score of
years. As if designed to test my worth, the emergency
bell rang, and I was at the door, anxious to serve, before
the bell had stopped ringing.

It was Bert Travers, the baker from the next street,
unshaven, tired, but with some inner relief on his face.
Could he have some barley water? You don't usually get

asked for that at this time in the morning, but I knew Bert's wife was desperately ill, and I would have done anything this glorious morning.

'How's the missus, Bert?' I asked.

'Through the crisis at last, thank God.'

'Good for Dr Wilkinson,' said I.

'No,' said Bert. 'Good for "him". He did it.'

'Dr Wilkinson's been out all night on a baby case. It was the vicar's stand-in. "He" came about seven o'clock last night and prayed by her bedside all night until an hour ago, when she came round from her coma. "*He*" pulled her through.'

'You say he's been with *you* all night, and has just left?'

'Yes,' said Bert. 'He told me he is leaving us for good today.'

Suddenly I realised that I had known all the time.

As soon as Bert had gone, I raced down to the station. The eight o'clock train was drawing out, and 'He' was standing at the carriage window.

When He saw me, He smiled and waved a gloved hand.

No one seemed to notice His going, but as with His sermons, He left His mark behind.

The vicar died under his operation, and now we have a young man who has done wonders with the Mother's Union and the Sunday School. I am still not a conventional church goer, but my wife and children are back, my business prospers and I am at peace with myself.

26. The Tree

L'ARBRE DE TENERE

*L'arbre de Tenere is the only named tree that
appears on topographical maps of Africa*

9 was doing my final year anatomy and physiology
when I met Mike Bullock. He was a final clinical year
student and we both played for the hospital rugby side.
He, as his name implies, was a big, solid, front-row
forward, while I fancied myself as a dashing wing three-
quarter.

He was one of those gentle giants who, whatever the
circumstances, could never be really provoked. A true
'man's man' – solid, pipe-smoking, six foot one inch,
and fifteen stone seven pounds in his socks. He was
neither very intelligent nor witty, but intelligent enough.
He had a slow, quiet smile and was at his happiest
bawling out coarse rugby songs with a pint of beer in
his hands. He was a sloppy dresser in an old tweed
sports coat with leather elbows, and shirts that could

have been slept in as well as lived in.

He was rambling on towards his finals when, with six months still to go, he made a complete change. He fell in love. Overnight he started to wear clean shirts and suits that had been made for him when he was two stone lighter.

The object of his love was the pretty, petite casualty staff nurse who had broken all our hearts. She was small and fragile and a complete contrast to her rugged partner. Her name was Penny.

The strange thing was that, in spite of the fact that she could have any student or consultant at her beck and call, there was no shadow of doubt that she loved him equally.

He was big and slow. She was small and fast. Walking together, it looked like a tug shepherding a liner into dock. He wore a look of dumb adoration on his face as if he just could not believe his good fortune.

They were inseparable. She came to all the rugby games; she washed his dirty shorts and socks.

When approaching them from a distance, you could not always see her because of his bulk, but when they got closer she was always there, darting around.

Penny had been the greatest flirt in the hospital, but after finding Mike she had eyes for him only. She knew he could not bear to be teased, so she did not try him.

There was something quite beautiful about seeing them together: this big adoring hulk and his will-o'-the-wisp flame. They planned to marry after qualifying, and Mike abandoned beer and games for the last three months' flog. His ever-attentive bride-to-be supplied coffee and sandwiches and sat up with him whilst he burnt the midnight oil.

Mike just qualified, which was enough, and by virtue

of my rugby prowess, I was asked to the coming dance.

I took along a little blonde midwife with whom I rather fancied my chances. And there was Mike, Dr Bullock now, beaming in a splendid new dinner jacket with his darling Penny on his arm; she was looking exotic, dressed in red chiffon.

It was a splendid night, with many hopeful travellers having arrived, and as alcohol and enthusiasms took over, it developed into a traditional, boisterous, glass-smashing, rugby-type party.

At 3.30 in the morning, there were just eight of us left, sitting in a corner, finishing a last bottle of champagne. Then, having downed it, we had no excuse to stay so we stumbled out into the cold air to find it was raining.

Mike and Penny were leading, walking unsteadily off the pavement to cross the road. They were halfway across when a taxi came skidding round and ploughed straight into them. It was difficult in the rain and dark to make out what had happened. One minute we were a happy fuddled lot emerging from the warmth of a happy evening, and the next we were in the midst of bloody screaming chaos.

The taxi had missed Mike but had almost cut Penny in two.

Mike picked her up.

She was screaming, with blood pumping from both severed femoral arteries, and Mike was stricken, baying 'Oh no! Oh no!'

By the time I reached them Penny's pulse was flickering and she was almost gone, her screams getting quieter, and Mike, this great house of a man, clutching this fragile wreck, tears pouring down his cheeks with his terrible sobbing cries.

In what must have been Penny's last moments, she

reached up, putting her arms round his neck, stroked his hair and talked gently and quietly into his ear. Then she was gone.

This was over thirty years ago, but I often relive the nightmare.

We had a terrible time with Mike. He would not let Penny go. Eventually, he carried her to an ambulance but sat holding her to him, dazed, looking into the distance and not speaking. Again, in the casualty department, he would not relax his grip, just sitting there covered by her blood, as if they were welded together. He would not speak or answer and eventually we gave him a shot of intramuscular sedative through the sleeve of his dinner jacket. After half an hour we were able to prise him off her.

Mike stayed in hospital for three days, not sleeping, hardly moving, just staring into space. Then on the third day, he got up, asked for his clothes, and disappeared for a couple of weeks.

Later I found he had sought out the stricken taxi driver who had caused the accident, and stayed with him and his wife and small daughter. I do not know if it was to comfort or share their grief, but I do know it would not be to blame.

A gaunt Mike returned to start his first hospital resident post three weeks later. He walked mechanically as if in a dream. A detail was worked out so that there was always one other resident with him to both watch him and his work.

There was a slow improvement. After six months he began to play rugby occasionally, but he was always withdrawn and you could never really get through to him. He would sit in a chair always edging over to the right side, smoking his pipe and drinking his beer, looking off into the distance, and if you spoke to him, it was always some time before he joined you in conversation.

Once, I passed his car on the sports ground and saw him sitting alone and smoking. Four hours later, I drove by again, and I think he had been sitting there on his own the whole time.

In 1939, the outbreak of war coincided with my failing my intermediate exam and I volunteered for the infantry. I was commissioned and six months later was posted to the Gouldshires to find that Mike Bullock was the regimental medical officer.

He had changed little. He had put on some weight, was less retiring, good natured, slow, but seemed still to look for opportunities to slip off and be on his own.

We were both at Dunkirk, but were taken off early and safely missed most of the bloodbath there.

It was different, both on D-Day and at the Rhine Crossing, when on both occasions nearly two-thirds of the regiment were slaughtered.

Mike was completely unmoved under fire. Although he did not take needless risks, he seemed to bear a charmed life, moving comfortably among the wounded, disregarding the bullets that were flying round.

I became as close to Mike as anybody could. We were the only two officers to survive the war out of the original muster of twelve that started out so hopefully in the spring of 1940.

We acquired the habit of being together and I was not irritated by his lack of communication, but treated him like a dependable bear who was always reassuringly at hand.

The freedom of war unsettled me and I decided to

give up medicine. I scratched around trying various things. Then in 1947, I got a job with a safari company who were exploring possible routes in North Africa with a view to attracting the American tourist market.

Mike and I were sharing a flat at the time. We got on easily, mainly because we did not intrude on one another's privacy. When I received this offer, he gave up his job as casualty officer at the Royal Naval Hospital and signed on as medical officer with the same company. Our equipment was all ex-War Department stuff and as the company had little capital, the quality of the vehicles was poor.

By late 1947, we were ready to set off in two trucks to pioneer the first trans-Sahara route.

There were six of us: two mechanics, a cook, a navigator (ex-RAF), myself as expedition leader, and Mike.

We motored leisurely down through France and Spain, getting to terms with our equipment, then crossed by boat from Gibraltar to Tangier. We had a pleasant drive through Morocco, along the coast road, into Algeria. We spent a week in Algiers, servicing our equipment, then in mid-January, headed south through Ghardia to El Golea and the end of the tarmacadam road and the start of the Sahara proper.

We had a short first day, following long tracks and acclimatising ourselves to desert conditions. We were given a most festive welcome by the French commander at Fort Mirabelle, a Foreign Legion fort seventy miles south of El Golea. He insisted we stay the night and set us up with maps, a great deal of advice and lent us a guide to take us 1,500 miles south down to Agades in Niger.

This was many years before Algeria and Niger gained their independence, and the French kept a tight control over desert traffic, mainly to prevent their limited resources from being overstretched on hopeless rescue attempts.

In the first year after the war, thirty-six families had died on the stretch of desert between El Golea and Tamanrasset, 800 miles south, not because of terrible desert conditions (it is a flat, rocky plateau) but because of travelling in faulty vehicles with inadequate provisions, petrol and water.

We had two Sappers as our mechanics, who kept the vehicles in tip-top condition, and we always carried at least a couple of days' spare water and petrol on each fifteen-hundredweight truck.

The journey down to Tamanrasset was a picnic. We were good company, time did not matter, and although the nights were cold, we had hot sunshine each day. This was mid-winter and the heat was like the very best days of an English summer, with clear blue skies. We would sleep out at night, looking up into the clear star-lit skies that seemed so much closer than at home.

Mike was as happy as I had known him since he had lost Penny. He had plenty of time to be on his own, and at night would slope off, putting his sleeping bag down about a couple of hundred yards away from where we were grouped round the trucks. He would lie, smoking his pipe, in the back of the truck, for hours as we ground across the desert tracks. I would not let him do his share of driving after the first day on the desert proper as, lost in thought, he nearly drove us into a ravine.

He was his usual good-natured self, doing the major share of the chores. And he was the only one of us who could communicate with Nesta, the Algerian guide lent by the French, who viewed us with suspicion as alcohol-drinking, pig-flesh eaters.

We travelled south through this wonderful vast new terrain, across 500 miles of the bleak Tedemait Plateau to the sand-blown oasis of Insalah, where we sat gravely with Arab dignitaries, having our first mint tea. Then we moved on to the warmth of the Arak Gorge, where we saw gazelle and mouflon (mountain sheep), into the rugged moon-like strata of the Hoggar Mountains, to the oasis of Tamanrasset, where we stopped to re-check equipment and explore the terrain.

The French had set out to make Tamanrasset a model oasis and it had tree-lined roads, and shops. It was 4,000 feet up and had a temperate climate. We spent two days on camels going up into the Hoggar Mountains to the hermitage of the French priest Charles Foucald, killed by uprising Senusi tribesmen in 1916, and now about to be canonised by the Roman Catholic Church. He lived for some years on barley and water, alone in a stark shack now inhabited by two monks, on a bleak rock point called Assekrem.

This place had some profound effect on Mike, and he insisted on staying on with the monks for a couple of days, and walked back the 60 kilometres alone, while we enjoyed the hotel at Tamanrasset that had those two priceless desert refreshments of a bath and a beer.

We set off south again after Tamanrasset, fit and tanned, and so far had no mechanical or health troubles. We passed through the most beautiful country yet, with great plains of golden sand interrupted by huge jutting outcrops of rock. We crossed the border at In Guzzam into Niger, and once over the bleak border terrain, we were in the scrubland of northern Niger, with game and nomadic Arabs and their flocks that drift endlessly to and fro across the Sahara searching for grazing.

Since Tamanrasset, Mike had changed. He became

cheerful, excited, sang in a deep throaty voice, and no longer sloped off with his sleeping bag at night. He cheerfully took the wheel and was more extrovert than at any time I had known him. He had a new energy and raced about, trying to do everything himself, as if he were in a hurry for us to get on.

The weather became much hotter as we progressed south, passing two waterholes, surrounded by milling cattle, camels and nomads. Then we were upon the unspoilt native market town of Agades.

I thought that camel caravans were a thing of the past, but we had the magnificent sight of three to four hundred camels coming into the huge market place to be off-loaded with their supplies of salt and dates. The caravans had come in after weeks of travel over difficult terrain, with men and beasts perishing on the way. Now they had reached their goal, the 'Fruits of Agades', and they could relax and barter for their grain before starting the terrible journey back. We joined in with them, sitting round twig fires, sipping mint tea cooked in enamel pots, swopping shirts for swords and knives.

Again Mike, who had no Arabic, seemed to have some special way of communicating with them. He would be missing most of the time, then suddenly appear out of some nomad tent, with Arab friends around him. As a doctor, he was a great success, and there was a long queue outside his truck every morning for medical attention.

This was a new Mike, jovial and alive, and I, who had known him for so long, did not know this elated mood.

We had intended going north from Agades on a route that led to Djanet in Algeria at the foot of the Tassili plateau, where we would climb to the plateau on foot, with pack donkeys, to see how accessible the famous

5,000-year-old Tassili frescoes (cave drawings) were as a tourist attraction.

This route had had no attention during the war, and the French refused to let us go on it. They said it had become impassable.

We were determined, having come so far, not to retrace our steps, and in the end, reluctantly, the French said that if we took their senior army guide, we could have their permission to travel to Djanet by going westward across the Tenere Desert to Bilma, then north through Dirkous, Sequedine, and the abandoned town of Djado.

The price quoted for the guide (only as far as Bilma) was astronomical and would represent a year's wages, though, with luck, we might do it in two days. It was explained that it might be some months before he was able to get a lift back.

We discussed the new proposal. The Tenere Desert is one of the most inhospitable deserts in the world. It is 500 miles of absolutely flat sand. In the middle is one brackish water well, the Acheggour Well, which is only as big as a table top, with a small hole in the top for buckets. This insignificant dot is marked on most maps of the world, probably because there is nothing else in the whole area to hang a name on. The natives call this the dreaded Tenere Desert because there is only this water-hole and on average there are two sand storms every three days sweeping across it with nothing to hinder them.

Of the six of us, three were for crossing and three were for going back. For once, Mike, who usually had no opinion, was all for crossing, and he eventually persuaded the reluctant three to try. It was agreed that we would have a go, on the understanding that if things got rough early on we would turn back.

We made ready for an early start and got off in the dark at 4 a.m. We picked up Fal Arno, the guide, who insisted on bringing his own food which, as far as I could see, consisted of a box of a type of doughnut and a 'Great Delicacy', a roast goat's head, which he explained in bad French he would be pleased to share with me, as I was the expedition leader.

The trucks were heavily laden and Fal did not approve. We had sixty gallons of water and sixty gallons of petrol each. The water would last us at least six days, and the petrol would do double the distance. If all went well, we should do it in two days.

We had a slow, difficult start, getting through the 60 miles of undulating scrub country before we got into the desert proper. Twice we had to dig out of soft sand, and there was one puncture to mend. Mike was a tower of strength. He practically lifted the truck on his own when we changed the wheel, and he was even more alert and vital than he had been for the previous few days.

Leaving the scrub, the flat, firm sandy plain stretched endlessly before us. We sped on at 50 miles an hour, ticking off mile after mile, going forward into nothingness. Whenever we stopped, Fal was nervous, walking around looking up at the sky, urging us to go on.

On the first day we covered 300 miles and camped on this flat open plain, scooping out shallow pits in the sand to put our sleeping bags in. All was fine. We had nearly conquered the Tenere. But Fal was unsettled, praying even harder than usual, with his forehead pressed in the sand towards Mecca.

We made another early start and were off in style with two trucks, speeding along in line abreast, a hundred yards apart, with two long plumes of sand dust stretching out behind us. It was great to be alive.

I reckoned we were about 100 miles from the Acheggour Well when the sky darkened. A cloud rose in front of us and, in a minute, a screaming, shrieking sand storm was on us. Just as it all began to black out, I saw the other truck lurch into the air before it cartwheeled on its side and disappeared. We slammed to a halt, desperately winding up the windows against the liquid sand that was pouring in. I turned to see Mike reaching for the first-aid kit. He slipped out of the back of the truck and went into the darkness. My 'bloody fool' was lost in the wind.

We sat encased in a whirling sea of sand for four hours. We wore scarves over our faces to prevent the fine particles getting into our lungs. Then, suddenly, as if a tap had been turned, the storm stopped and once again we were in the middle of a sunny windless plain.

We scrambled over to the mound that was the other truck. The occupants were all right, though the cook had a badly bruised arm.

Mike had not reached them. We found his body half covered in sand. He was lying on his side and a great pile of sand had blown up against his broad shoulders. Both of his arms were bent, and it looked as if he was holding someone, protecting them from the wind. One can let one's imagination run riot, and everything was distorted by the sand, but he had a look of smiling peace on his face.

Fal Arno brought out a shovel and began digging a grave. The Arabs are philosophical and unemotional about death. They believe that, at some time, every man's time comes and we cannot influence it. It is decided for us. As far as Fal Arno was concerned, Allah had deigned that this was Mike's time and there was nothing to be done about it.

We buried him with a simple prayer and, as is the desert custom, threw a handful of thorn twigs and some date stones into his grave.

We dug out the trucks and, towing the second one, we limped passed the Acheggour Well safely into Dirkou. We reported Mike's death to the authorities, who seemed little interested. Then we went on to complete the rest of our journey north to Djanet and then back to Algiers, then a week by boat home.

The route we had pioneered became a regular safari run and each February, parties of twelve or so rich Americans are chauffeured round it with their cameras.

I had to find new routes so did not return to this area for seven years. Since then, every February, it has been a routine trip for me.

Crossing the Tenere for the first time again after this lapse, I re-visited the spot, of which I had taken a bearing, where we had buried Mike, and on that spot a tree was growing.

In the desert, when a man or beast dies, he is buried with thorn sticks and date stones. He is put back into the earth that he came from with the hope that he will give the sustenance for fresh life to spring from the earth again and help man to fight his eternal battle with nature.

This tree had become a holy place for the Arabs, and every beat-up caravan crossing the Tenere Desert, four days out from the Acheggour Well, would stop there for prayer. And, however little water they had, a goatskin of this desert gold was poured into its roots before they passed on, and so it had flourished.

There are many things we do not understand, but I believe that when Penny was dying, she realised that Mike could not bear to be without her, and in her last minute, when she took him in her arms, she told him she would never leave him. And in some strange way she never did.

I think that when he sloped off on his own or sat on his own, it was to be with her, and I think she was with him.

I think that he had been waiting all these years to join her.

There were many times he could have opted out, particularly during the war, but this would not have done in their sort of relationship. He just had to wait patiently until his time came.

When we found his body in the sand with his arm bent, I think that it was not that he was protecting her from the wind, I think it was Penny welcoming him into her arms at last.

I have travelled this route for the last fifteen years now and as all the caravans stop there, life has started to grow round the tree. There are always enough thorn twigs for a fire, and it is a place of rest and refreshment.

I like to think that they are there together and each February, when I lead my party through the Tenere, I don't have to find my way to the tree. When I am within fifty miles of it, my scalp begins to tingle. I am guided to it like a beacon and there is an air of happiness and welcome when I get there.

Now I am probably a romantic old fool and this is all in my imagination. Perhaps I have been too long in the desert. But camel caravans have crossed this desert for some thousands of years and in the same way as they are crossed now. The only difference is that now, someone might have a transistor radio and some smoke. During those years, scores of thousands of men and animals have perished making the crossing. Each has been buried in exactly the same way as Mike Bullock was, with a handful of date stones and a few thorn twigs.

But as any traveller you might meet who has the misfortune to cross this desolate waste will confirm: there is only one tree in the Tenere Desert.

27. A Husking of Fears

As I took the road for the Western Highlands, I
realised the depths of my despair. My senior
partner had sent me off for a few days to try and find
myself and to get over the mood of depression and
despair I had drifted into.

I am the junior partner in a large medical practice in
the north of England. I had started my first post full of
hope and determination, but as I became involved with
the affairs of my patients I found I got far too near to
their problems. I tried to be all things to all men. I
expected, with my faith and skill, to give some sort of
divine judgment to resolve people's difficulties. Instead,
I found myself in a supporting role, a continual giving
of energy and propping against problems that had no
answers. I was with people who had to go on living lives
with nothing apparently to hope for.

I poured out my energy, making no change on the face
of the scene, and wondered how I personally would have
coped with the events on which I was giving such
profound advice. There seemed to be no happy endings.

I had run myself so low that I had stopped believing in both myself and in what I was doing. I was obviously worrying my partners as I was summoned to a practice meeting which resulted in my senior partner giving me the orders for my journey.

As I drove north, the lowlands seemed wet and bleak. It was early spring and the countryside had not yet grown its new rich coat of green. As I began to climb through the foothills, I entered great banks of mist. I drove with my headlights on, snug in the warm shell of the car.

Eventually, I was groping my way through a great white cloud. I crept along only just seeing the road. It seemed endless and, steadily climbing, I became lost in time and space. Then abruptly, I was out of it. I seemed to have entered another world. I stopped the car, opened the window, and looked out in wonderment.

The sun was shining, the grass was green. It looked as if spring had already visited here. Stretching up majestically in front of me were the highland mountains and their snow-capped peaks. I lit my pipe and admired the view whilst the smell of new heather crept into the car.

The countryside ahead was empty, but I was conscious of something. I looked round and there, standing about two yards from my offside wheel, was a girl. Her large brown suitcase was kept together round the middle with a white strap. I could not believe she had been there all the time. But where had she come from? She smiled. A confusion of faces and names rushed through my mind. Did I know her?

I wound down the window. 'Excuse me,' I said, 'your name wouldn't be Wainwright, would it?'

She smiled as if she had been asked this sort of

question a thousand times before. 'I'm sorry. No,' she said.

I had my first proper look at her. She was quite beautiful. Her looks and her smile overwhelmed me. I cannot describe a beautiful painting, all I am able to record is the amount of pleasure it gives, looking at it. If I looked across a crowded hall, this is the one face I would see.

I said, 'If you would care to join me for lunch . . . if we can find a place. I shall be driving round the mountains this afternoon and would be delighted to show you, if that's what you've come to see.'

She said, 'I really want to see what the buses are doing. But I would be grateful for a lift.'

I put her suitcase on the back seat and we drove off. Normally I am shy with the opposite sex, but we talked easily together as if we were resuming an interrupted conversation.

We stopped at a very unpromising-looking pub for a drink. When we were leaving, she said, 'I would like to have lunch with you.' We drove on until we came to a grey, sombre-looking hotel.

Having entered the even greyer doors of this remote hostelry, we were suddenly in a delightful dining place with red-coated waiters and sophisticated bars. There was a great wide staircase leading to the accommodation above.

Looking back, it seems incredible that those outer walls could have contained such magnificence. We dined on the most superb food and wines and I finished my lunch with one of her cigarettes. I was entranced by my companion, but I did not marvel at the impossibility of it all.

In the afternoon, we drove round the winding roads,

getting out to climb when the sun shone, then hurriedly running back into the intimacy of the car when it rained. Sitting inside the car, we were shut off in a little world of our own. We sat, caressing each other with our eyes, then emboldened, I touched her cheek. When I put my head forward, our lips brushed gently.

I stretched my arm round her and she came into the hollow of my arm, resting her forehead on the flesh of my neck. She was cool and soft. She said, 'What about next year and the year after? Surely this isn't just for now.'

'No,' I said. 'This will last. I see it stretching before me. I cannot see the end.'

She moved closer into my warmth.

We were not alone in the hills. There were streams of anonymous cars with anonymous people, crawling up the steep roads. But we were detached, parked in a lay-by, in a world of our own.

We decided to stay at the hotel where we had eaten, where the splendour was exotic and out of place. The smart waiters smiled kindly at us. They had seen couples like us before.

She came to my room after dinner and we kissed briefly as we had done in the afternoon. We gravely examined each other's hands and faces, tracing their outline with gentle fingertips, searching for hidden secrets. She stood and I held her to me, feeling her body melt into mine.

She half-stood back, still supported by my arms, and placed a finger on my lips. 'Tonight is too soon, my love. I must go before it is too late for both of us.' And she hurried out, leaving half her presence with me.

We met at breakfast, and she was even lovelier, if that were possible. Then I saw a trace of sadness in her eyes.

My leaping concern showed as she said, 'Don't worry. I just woke with a little fear this morning. It will pass.'

We spent the day roaming the hills. We returned for meals, thinking we were hungry, but when the exotic food was in front of us, we had no appetite. We both knew that the evening would bring the coming together we had postponed from the night before.

In the afternoon, sitting on a grassy bank, I said, 'I have waited so many years for you. Why didn't you come before?'

She said, 'You weren't ready for me. You had so many mistakes to make, so many false trails to follow, so many people you tried to make look like me. If you had come before, it would have been too soon. If you had come tomorrow, it would have been too late. These things are decided for us. I only found you myself when I wasn't looking. It is only when we come to know the real that we can see how far from the real we were before.'

That night she came shyly to my room. The rest of her beauty was like her face and hands. Soon her slender body was lost in my embrace. I had read that love was a lusty, virile thing, but I found that it was tender consideration that took us to the heights we reached. I cannot believe that anyone could become closer than we became as our very being seemed to hover in the room.

She left me before dawn but I could still breathe her substance when she had gone.

The next day we could not bear to be apart. If I could not touch her, then at least my chair must be touching hers. We drifted through the day, adoring each other. I had been unaware before what a capacity for love we have.

That night she came to me again, with the knowledge of the night before behind us, and we became lost together in a gentle, intertwining dream. As we parted, she told me that in the afternoon she had the terrible sensation of what it would be like without me. I hushed her fears, comforting her slenderness in the strength of my arms.

The next day drifted by in this idyll of loved companionship. That night she came to my door, holding herself tight, draining off her desire. 'Tonight, my love, I must rest. I cannot stay with you.'

I, who had never cried before, wept my heart into the bed. I knew that on the next day we would both have to journey on from wherever we had come. I must have slept, for I woke at 5 a.m. with a terrible tearing pain in my chest. Oh, God, I thought, she's dead. But all was quiet, and I had no excuse for stealing to her room. I thought if I could wait until six, perhaps I could go and see her then. At quarter to, I stole down to the kitchen and lifted a great kettle onto the flat black stove. As I lifted it, my hand caught on the flat black innocuous top. I screamed inwardly with pain as I felt the back of my left hand burning. I snatched it away to see a crop of fiery blisters forming. I bound my hand with some tape, made some coffee, and took it to her room. She was sleeping.

I kissed the warmth of her face until she was awake.

She said, 'I am pleased I was asleep. I would have hated to awaken on my own, knowing I was going.' She looked up. 'Oh, my love, you have been crying. Don't be sad. This is just the beginning.'

'But what about the middle and the end?' I said.

She replied, 'The middle will be like the beginning and there will be no end.'

'But, having found you, if I were to decide to live forever and you ever should leave me, I would be left to face eternity alone.'

She took my face in her hands. She said, 'My love, though I have to go, I will never leave you, nor you me. If you reach out your hand, you will always find me.'

I lay with her for an hour, my head on the softness of her breast. Then I carried her case down to the bus, and she was gone.

I drove back to the practice, to find that I had been away four days. I was somewhat confused as I remembered, during those days, having champagne with the word 'fifty' and deep red flowers with the word 'sixty'. These were anniversaries of hours together, but could just have easily been weeks, months or years; time had somehow lost its meaning.

As she promised, she was with me.

When I was driving, I could feel her by my side. I resolved then to keep my car until mechanical skills could no longer keep it on the road just in case, in another car, I should not find her with me when I drove.

At night, if I lay on my left side and crossed my arms with resting finger on my brow, I felt I was holding her. Our touch was as one.

I looked for quiet moments on my own when I could savour her presence. I did not even have to reach out to her; it was as if part of her were with me and I could turn my cheek to feel the cool of her brow.

I found a new patience with my work. The unbearable became bearable. While she was with me, I could suffer no hurt. I had a new strength and I began to grow towards the shape of man I had always wanted to be. But I did not understand it. And I was afraid to drive north in case I found no place where we had been.

In the middle of last night in a dimly lit cottage, too remote to be reached by electricity, I was desperately trying to find a vein in the arm of an old man, fighting for his breath. His terrified wife at last held my torch still enough for me to find a vein and to inject a relieving drug. I injected slowly and as he responded to the drug, his breathing began to improve. After ten minutes my injection was completed and his breathing was normal, panic over. As I withdrew the needle from his vein the torch was shining on my hands. I looked down and there on the back of my left hand was the scar of the burn.

Finale

28. Playing at Writing

Playing at writing is perhaps as good a form of relaxation as most. It has the advantage of allowing you scope outside your own particular work environment without leaving that environment or necessarily interfering with it.

The difficulties presented to a doctor-author are that, as writing about subjects you are familiar with is the easiest way of getting into print, whatever your original intention, such is the insatiable lay public's appetite for medicine of one sort or another, you are soon sidetracked into writing medicine of one sort or another.

My own sorties into the world of writing have been as a funny man. I think I'm a side-splitter, but whenever I have been fortunate enough to have one of my gems of wit accepted, be it writing, radio or television, the pattern has always been the same. The acceptor doubled up with laughter as we went over the selected script, then immediately tried to sign me up to write a second Dr Spock. Thus a long-worked-on humorous column in a national daily brought an immediate commission for two articles for a mother and baby-care magazine: 'Is Your Midwife a Personal Friend?' and 'What to Do for the Colicky Baby'.

A TV interview about a 'funny' published book established me as the resident doctor on the 'Diary' programme for the same channel, answering viewers' medical problems.

Using a different pseudonym for every different piece you write offers some protection, and recently I have been writing a weekly column under my wife's maiden name, supposedly as the mother of two children, with her mother living with us, and my aged parents dropping in from time to time to see us.

I am only allowed to do this, of course, on the condition that I deal clearly with the day-to-day paediatric-geriatric crises that arise as a major part of my narrative. That this particular magazine, which has been going since World War I, prints its final issue next month is probably all my fault.

Writers fall into many categories, and range from the creative novelist to hack journalist, the latter category being the one I ascribe to, and just getting into print does not mean one is an author. But it is fun to have appeared in print enough to be able to enjoy the company of writers. It is also a great help in becoming completely schizophrenic as you soon find that, in the company of doctors, they think of you as a writer, and in the company of writers, they think of you as a doctor.

Describing your own experiences in your own words is probably the best way of starting to write. It can have a specific quality of its own, and as a doctor one has this unique access into people's homes and lives, providing original material in the most marketable writing commodity of all, medical drama.

There is tremendous scope in translating routine medicine into lay language for radio, television and the printed word.

The commonest problem for which advice is asked from the editor of a child-care magazine has never reached me in the surgery, and radio and television are the only means of communication with some sections of the community. I feel there is great scope for the presentation of simple preventive medicine via both these media. They offer opportunities to explain and reassure, and this seems of much greater value than the showing of the latest cardiac transplant techniques in detail and technicolour.

Writing lay medicine, however, has its own problems. It is difficult to find something fresh to say about measles the eighth time you write about it; even pregnancy, with all its variations, can be trying, and your writing can easily become just an extension of your everyday work.

There is tremendous demand from various types of magazines, particularly mother and baby-care and women's magazines, for medical articles. Rates of pay are generally good, and the writing serves some purpose. If one's aesthetic senses are not always satisfied, it is pleasant when taking out friends for a night in the West End, to know that it is being paid for by your thousand words on athlete's foot.

If you decide, as a doctor, that you want to play at writing or broadcasting, by the nature of the subject you have been trained in, you are in a far more advantageous position to enjoy some success in it than any other profession. It has its dangers, in that too soon you can become an instant authority on practically any subject.

I was once commissioned to write a light-hearted

article on sex education. I realised that this was impossible, but with the coaxing of a first-class editor eventually a reasonably commonsense article was produced. Its value was that I, the author, started out without knowledge or much prejudice to present and translate the pros and cons of this subject into a language I had acquired some experience in using. On the strength of this article I was invited to take part in a radio panel discussion of the same subject, the other members being a housewife, a schoolmaster, and the chairwoman – a well-known radio and television personality. To my horror, halfway through the discussion, the panel chairwoman turned to me as *the expert*, asking me to give my views to the listening two and a half million. It is sometimes not enough to know that you are not.

In two short months I had changed from an enquirer into an unexplored subject to a national authority. Within two further weeks I had mothers quoting me to me, myself. It was only my pseudonym that saved me. Further experience has taught me how to avoid such situations.

Writing has established a firm hold on me, and now one working day of each week is put aside for it.

What motivates one to write, broadcast or appear on television is difficult to ascertain. Some are creative artists, and this is their medium of expression; it is essential for others in completing their own ego; for many it is their best or only way of making or supplementing a living; a select few have some sincere message they have to spread. In examining my own motivation, and having examined all the possible reasons, I am left with the chastening thought that it is most likely because I love the sound of my own voice.